ROSE-COLOURED LOVE

Devan didn't want her past to catch up with her. Hadn't she spent a year trying to forget, trying to rekindle her talent, to no avail? Why wouldn't the stranger just take no for an answer and go away?

Books you will enjoy
by AMANDA CARPENTER

WAKING UP

For Robbie time seemed to have drifted past, and she still didn't know what she wanted to do with her future. Just because Jason had his future mapped out didn't mean she should go along with him – but then Jason was acting very strangely these days . . .

CAPRICE

Pierce had not been expected to attend the party, so Caprice, normally so self-assured, was taken by surprise when she was literally swept into the arms of this unknown man who made her feel so different, so out of control . . .

GIFT OF HAPPINESS

Katherine was afraid that by asking Luke to help her escape, she was leading him into danger. But he was the only person she felt she could trust – and maybe find a little happiness with . . .

ROSE-COLOURED LOVE

BY

AMANDA CARPENTER

MILLS & BOON LIMITED
15–16 BROOK'S MEWS
LONDON W1A 1DR

First published in Great Britain 1986
by Mills & Boon Limited

© Amanda Carpenter Ltd. 1986

Australian copyright 1986
Philippine copyright 1987
This edition 1987

ISBN 0 263 75574 6

Set in Times 11¼ on 12 pt.
01-0287-44623

Computer typeset by SB Datagraphics,
Colchester, Essex

Printed and bound in Great Britain by
Collins, Glasgow

CHAPTER ONE

'No, I'm sorry, she doesn't live here,' said Devan politely to the stranger.

'But, D——' said the child beside her, puzzled, and Devan silenced her with the nudge of her foot.

She stood lounging against the doorpost while she spoke through the screen door to him. He was a large, solid shadow in comparison with the sunny golden light spilling all over the scene beyond the covered porch, but what she could see of him was pleasing enough. He was well dressed, well groomed, his rather light brown hair blown to chaos from the wind, his sleeves rolled up in the heat of the day. She couldn't really see much of his facial features because of the shadow, but the sun behind him lit his jaw to perfect illumination, showing it square and firm. The gleaming car behind him sported rent-a-car plates. She glanced at it, a bit wryly. A hundred-dollar-a-day fare for that one, if she'd have her guess.

Eight-year-old Janie had subsided and contented herself with sticking her finger up her nose, which Devan jerked down. The man was replying, blankly, 'Doesn't live here?' He swivelled on one foot to look behind him at the country road, the dilapidated letter box which showed no numbering, the empty expanse to either side of the house.

'Isn't this 1505 Elm Road?'

Janie pinched Devan in the leg, and Devan retaliated by laying a very heavy hand on the girl's shoulder. She had caught a quick flash at his profile but it was enough. Authority, decision, and determination were stamped on those features, or she'd eat her socks. Whoever was he?

'This is Elm Road, all right,' she replied laconically, when he had whirled back to her in impatience. She turned to look up the patched, narrow road for a few drawn-out moments, contemplatively, drawing out her response as long as she could, with a wicked enjoyment. 'But this isn't 1505. This is 1509.'

Janie made a noise, and Devan tightened her hand. She watched the man raise his hand and thrust his fingers through the thick hair at his forehead. He looked hot, baffled, and furious. 'Damnation, how did that happen?' he said disgustedly. 'I passed 1503 some time ago, but there isn't another house between that one and this.' He glanced at the two obscured by screening and, though his eyes were in shadow, she caught the glittering brightness of that look. He said softly, even gently, 'Are you sure this isn't where Devan Richardson lives?'

'We're proof positive,' said Devan without a bat of an eye, inclining her head to him.

Janie's carrot-red head swivelled to her, and the child asked suspiciously, 'What's that?'

She said out of the corner of her mouth, 'I'll explain later.' Then she let go of the girl's shoulder, crossed her arms, and kicked one foot over the other and, with a remarkably charming smile, she said commiseratingly to the stranger, 'They never use logic in planning street addresses.'

The stranger narrowed his eyes on her, running his gaze from head to bottom, consideringly. 'Well,' he said finally, with a flashing white smile, 'please forgive me for disturbing you.'

'No problem,' said she, not moving. He turned and ran down the four painstakingly swept porch steps and went to his car, a swift, athletic, definitely eye-catching figure, and then he slipped into his car and reversed down the gravel driveway. She shut and locked the door behind him, her lower lip thrust out in deep thought. Who could it have been? She didn't remember having ever met the man before and, aside from her excellent memory for names and faces, she would never have forgotten a man like him. He was the type of person one watched out for, remembered, the type that was going somewhere and going fast, the type that moved mountains and restructured planes of thinking.

He was the type of person she had once been.

'You told a fib,' said Janie accusingly, as Devan moved away from the door. 'In fact, you told several. Aunt Devan, I'm gonna tell Mom.'

'What, so she can beat me?' retorted Devan, who stopped to turn around and face her niece anyway. She put on her stern expression as she faced her freckled accuser, and lectured, 'Now, look, Janie, just because I told a fib doesn't mean it's right, or that you can start telling them!'

'Then what you did was wrong,' Janie stated positively, and Devan sighed.

'You know, it probably was, but I have to work that out myself,' she continued, and then stopped, wondering what to say next. She sighed again. 'Look, it was the only thing I could think of to get him to go away. I don't want to see him, and I don't have to if I don't want to. Remember that, kiddo. You don't have to talk to strangers if you don't want to.'

'Then why didn't you just tell him to go away?' asked Janie, shifting from one bare foot to the other.

'Somehow,' said Devan drily, 'I doubt he would have taken that as an answer.' She became suddenly brisk. 'And he's going to be back, just as soon as he's found out that I lied, so we're going to close the windows and curtains and lock the doors.'

Janie's face grew mulish. 'I wanted to go outside.'

'You can later.' The girl didn't move. 'Come on, Janie, please! He's going to be back any minute now! We can watch for him upstairs, OK?'

The girl wavered, and then grinned, showing a toothy truce, and she said, 'OK!'

Devan watched her run up the stairs, and then moved unhurriedly through the ground floor of the comfortable farmhouse, making sure the back door was locked and the windows latched. How could she possibly explain to an eight-year-old child that she had no intention of talking to that man, or anyone else for that matter who might possibly have known of her and her former profession?

Her former life. Devan stopped at the bottom of the staircase as she thought of that, stopping quite still, not even breathing, stopping with the utter immobility of one that feels a mortal wound and is stricken with the realisation, and the pain. Then, breathing slowly and evenly, she climbed the stairs to the first floor. There she went strolling along to her bedroom, which faced the front of the house. Sure enough, Janie was pressing her snub nose to the glass of her window, sprawled in the one chair in the room. Devan threw herself on to her wide double bed and listened to the springs creak, feeling the mattress sway.

'Ain't here yet,' said Janie.

'Isn't,' Devan corrected absently. She crossed her arms behind her head and stretched out her legs. 'Let me know when you see him.' That man, he certainly wasn't from the area. Oh no, not he; he was the New Yorker type. There was no way a man such as that would be content to live in small town, U.S.A. This part of Maine was the quiet life personified. Absolutely and unalterably no future here.

At least not for her. Paris trotted in through the open doorway and leapt on to the bed. She turned her head and smiled at the battered, scar-faced tomcat as, with motor already purring in high gear, he circled around neatly and then settled, closing his one good eye in bliss. Devan had named the stray tomcat Paris in a fit of gleeful irony after that lusty Trojan lover who had stolen Helen from her husband, the event which had been the blithe start to the epic Trojan war. Her sister Helen hadn't thought much of the idea at the time, but treated the cat well in spite of it, and the name had stuck like glue. She scratched at the tom's ragged ear, making him bare his throbbing throat in ecstasy; that this particular lover had been in many wars, Devan hadn't a doubt.

Through the closed window, Devan could already hear the unmistakable sounds of gravel crunching under heavy car tyres, and she turned her head to Janie. With a sigh, she crossed her ankles and said mildly, 'I hope that's not your mom, or we're both in trouble.' Paris stopped purring, now fast asleep.

'No,' said Janie to the glass, with every sign of fascination, 'it's that man.'

Devan sat up sharply. 'Then come away from the window.'

'Oh, Aunt Devan, I wanna watch——' complained the girl.

'Janie!' She watched her niece snap out of the chair at the tone she used, so she softened her voice. 'That's better.' Janie sniffed. 'Oh, come on. Now, if you'll just be quiet a litle longer, I'll play Monopoly with you.'

That brightened the girl's face immeasurably. 'I'll go and get it!' she cried, and bounced to the hallway.

'Wait!' said Devan. They both listened to the

sounds of deliberate footsteps on the wooden porch, and then there was a sharp staccato knock at the front door.

'It's in the hall cupboard,' said Janie. 'He won't see me.' She whisked out of the room while Devan closed her eyes and mildly hoped that the girl was right. Soon Janie was back, and they set up the board game on Devan's bed. The knocking continued for a very long time, much longer than she'd have expected, even from someone with as determined a jaw as he'd had. Then it stopped, only to start again at the back door. Devan dealt out the money, and Janie picked out her favourite playing piece, the little dog, while Devan took the top hat. The knocking continued on and on, until she thought she might scream.

Even Janie got exasperated, and snapped as she scratched her bare ankle, 'Why won't he just go away?'

'You can go first, we don't have to roll for it,' murmured Devan distractedly. Her patience was fast ebbing away, and she gritted her jaw while her eyes grew a bit wild. The next instant, she was thrusting off her bed with a bounce that sent playing cards scattering, and she marched to the upstairs bathroom with grim intent. 'That does it!'

Janie, and then Paris, trailed behind. 'What're you gonna do, Aunt Devan?'

'Something wicked.' She whirled around and grabbed Janie's shoulders and at first shook her niece, and then hugged her tight. Then she said sternly, 'Don't do as I do, you do as I say!'

With that rather cryptic remark, Janie, not in the least put out by her eccentric aunt's behaviour, just smiled and settled back to observe events. Devan whisked out a plastic bucket, used for washing the hardwood floors, from the hall cupboard, and ran to the bathroom to turn the bath taps on full blast. The bucket was filled within a few seconds, and she marched through the upstairs hall with her two shadows. Picking Helen's bedroom, which was over the kitchen, she found a window that overlooked the back door. She threw it open. The persistent knocking was much louder with the window open. She took the bucket and held it just outside, and then neatly flipped it over. The water cascaded out. The knocking abruptly stopped. Devan stuck out her furious face and saw that the strange man was quite drenched, so the water must have hit dead on target. He was staring quite calmly up.

'Go away!' Devan shouted at him, upset by his calm demeanour and her own impulsiveness. He opened his mouth to say something, but she popped her head back in and slammed the window shut so that the glass vibrated dangerously. Then she turned and stared, terrified at herself and her giggling niece. She snapped, 'Do you want to play Monopoly or not?' And she stalked back to her bedroom.

Later, after Helen had come back from the visit to the dentist with her youngest child, Gary, they were all sitting down to dinner. Gary was two years younger than Janie, who was convinced he was the bane of her existence, which, as Devan thought back to her own childhood and how she had treated her older sister, seemed to her fair enough.

Helen, much too young and pretty to be a widowed mother of two, and much too wise to show her children that she knew it, asked placidly, 'So what did you two do while Gary and I were at Dr Long's?'

Janie immediately choked on her glass of milk and looked as guilty as sin, at which Gary hooted, and Devan laid her head down on the table. 'Janie,' she said, resigned now that her sister's suspicions were fully aroused 'you have about as much finesse as an elephant.'

'What's finesse?' Janie asked, her brow wrinkled. Then she said frustratedly, 'You never call me anything I can understand!'

Devan looked stricken at this foul play on her part. Helen said mildly, 'Gary, eat your peas. They're getting cold.'

The tow-headed boy looked at his plate in some surprise as though he'd expected the peas to start sprouting. Then he whistled through the gap in his front teeth, a recent addition as of that very afternoon. Devan said to Janie, 'I'm sorry. Finesse means means delicacy. No, that's not quite it, but it's close enough.'

'How can an elephant be delicate?' asked Janie, and Devan gave it up thankfully. Gary then took his spoon and smashed it into the offending peas. Everyone stopped dead, and three pairs of wide eyes turned to Helen to see how she would mete out justice for such a flagrant sign of defiance.

Helen raised her auburn, sleek eyebrows slowly as she considered her fast-wilting son, and Devan quickly hid her face in her coffee cup. Then her sister said calmly, 'You still have to eat your peas, whether they're mashed, or not.' Gary ducked his head, and everyone started to breathe again. But if Devan and Janie thought that they were off the hook by Gary's timely diversion, they were sadly mistaken, for then Helen turned to her daughter and repeated, 'What *did* you two do this afternoon, anyway?'

Janie looked to her aunt in desperation, who rubbed at her eyes and then told her, 'There are times, Janie, when you should *never* lie, and this is one of them.' Devan turned to a very interested Helen, and told the whole story reluctantly, and afterwards there was a little silence, filled, on Gary's part, with something close to awe for his aunt.

Helen searched Devan's eloquent eyes thoughtfully, with some concern. Finally she turned to her daughter and said emphatically, 'You should never do as your aunt does, you do as she says.'

Janie looked utterly disgusted. 'That's what *she* said!'

After the evening meal, the children scampered off for their nightly hour of television. The dishes were still on the table, for it was Devan's job to wash up. She lounged broodingly in her chair, waiting for Helen to say something more about the afternoon's episode, but her older sister just stared into space and sipped at her coffee.

Helen said softly, 'I wish you'd eat more.' Devan
looked at her untouched meal expressionlessly.
'I'm worried about you.'

Then it was Devan who said, with her eyes on
the table, 'I should never have acted that way in
front of Janie. I'm sorry, it won't happen again.'

That caused a slow smile to cross Helen's face.
'That I doubt, as long as you have a temper to
misplace. I—guess I hadn't realised how adamant
you really are about not seeing anyone from New
York.'

That brought Devan's head up with a snap, and
her eyes narrowed. 'You didn't have anything to do
with that stranger coming here, did you?' she
queried, and her soft voice was dangerous.

But her older sister looked immensely surprised.
'Good heavens, no! I respect your desires more
than that; you should know that!'

Devan looked and felt ashamed. 'I know. I just
can't figure out who he would be, and it doesn't
make sense that he was someone from the area. It's
probably nothing.'

'You were abominably rude,' said Helen matter-
of-factly, by which she was putting the subject
behind her. 'God only knows, he can't possibly
want to come back for more! Just forget about it,
Devan.' That last was said gently, though Devan's
face never changed; her sister knew her that well.
'Don't let it haunt you any more than you can.'

Then her sister was rising to supervise bathtime
for the two children, and Devan was left staring at

nothing, nothing at all. She had known what Helen had meant by that last statement, and it hadn't anything to do with that afternoon. She heard the three clatter upstairs. Then she pushed away from the table and forced herself to stack the dishes and begin washing up.

The silence and hot water were both making her sleepy. She was always affected this way by the country air. It was lulling; no city noises to spur one on, no late night honking and beeping, no light-splashing neon signs. She sighed—it seemed as if she was always sighing—and she hung her head like a dead weight on her neck as she scrubbed listlessly at the last pot with her heat-reddened hands.

The sun had gone down a long time ago, and blackness reigned outside. She started another full pot of coffee. She went through a ritual every time the sun went down, going through the two downstairs rooms that she had converted into a library on her arrival. She would pick masters off the shelf. Wordsworth, Longfellow, even Hemingway she would read, draining endless cups of coffee, listening to the orchestrated chirrup of hidden rasping insects, sometimes with Paris on her knee, sometimes without him. Then, on other days, she would take from the shelves George Macdonald's *Lilith* and *Phantastes*, those battered, dog-eared pages, yellowing, coffee-stained, thumb-printed, and she would read the words she knew by heart. Some days she would choose the sensuality of D. H. Lawrence, or the mastery of Shakespeare, whispering the powerful, stark prose or verse with pain and enjoyment. They were her friends, those books.

Exquisite tormentors, those books.

Finished, she turned at random and walked over to sink into one of the kitchen chairs, her hands limp. Helen never understood her. But then, at the same time, her sister didn't question or nag, and Devan was immensely thankful for it. Helen just surrounded her with the same steady compassion and affection that she gave to her two erratic offspring, and Devan's days were now filled with serene, soul-healing peace, except that her soul never seemed to heal.

The nights were the worst. Sometimes she would rage, prowling through the downstairs rooms like a caged beast, the taut bitterness making her neck muscles ache as though ripped. At other times she just—existed. For it was gone; it had left her desolate and wondering why, and she could not find it anywhere: her words, her writing, her lovely children of the night, those past and flame-filled evenings when she would blaze far into the darkness with the heat and brilliance of *her* intensity, *her* conviction, *her* magnificent, marvellous myths.

Ah! She thrust herself off the chair with carefully controlled yet violent movements. No use thinking of it, no use any of it, no use thinking. How could Helen understand a passion she had never experienced before? She simply couldn't, and Devan was ragged from the haunting she could not seem to ease.

Paris was sleeping, stretched across the doorway to the hall, and Devan reached down to ruffle at his head roughly, making him wake with a caterwauling start. It was time to give him supper. And though he might squirm with the restless desire to prowl his outside domain, this battered king, she would keep him caged along with her tonight, for she did not wish to be alone.

She turned and started a new tin of cat food whirring through the tin opener, and now, fully awake, Paris rubbed against her legs with an excess of affection. She set his dish down, and he went for it like a starving thing.

Light footsteps racing along the hall, and then Devan was overwhelmed by both Gary and Janie who hurled against her for an exuberant good night hug. She ruffled Gary's head, and pressed a quick kiss against Janie's carrot head, for Gary wouldn't let anyone kiss him except for Helen, and her only occasionally. Helen stood at the doorway smiling, but as Devan's head raised again, she saw her sister dart a quick glance at the full, waiting pot of coffee.

'OK, that's it, kids,' said Helen, with a clap of her hands when the two appeared disposed to linger. 'Now, upstairs with the both of you—go on, scat! I'll be up in a few minutes to tuck you both in and kiss you good night. Pick up your feet, Gary; don't scuffle like that.'

And so, with a great and obvious reluctance to

end their day, as they were reluctant to end all their days, the two trudged upstairs again, with many a long-suffering, soulful look cast behind them. The looks fell off their mother's shoulders like rain, and Devan had to smile.

But Helen wasn't as she asked diffidently, 'Late night again?'

Devan's smile disappeared, and she turned to fiddle with a cupboard door, bringing down a coffee cup and setting it carefully beside the coffee pot. 'I'm not very sleepy,' she said quietly.

And just as quietly, Helen said, 'You don't sleep, you don't eat, you don't go anywhere——'

'Don't——' Devan grated, raising a hand as she whirled around to face Helen, who stopped. She continued, more calmly, 'Don't push, all right? Besides, look who's talking. You don't go any-where or do anything, either.'

She watched her sister smile, a little sadly, and she suddenly wondered who the sadness was for, herself or Helen. 'To you, it seems I never go anywhere,' returned her sister. 'I go out when I wish. But the difference, my dear, is that I have two somethings to keep me home.' Devan looked away. Then, in an entirely different tone of voice, Helen said, 'Oh, good! I see you've fed Paris. Well, then, I guess I'm on my way to a long, leisurely soak in the bath, and then bed.'

'So early?' Devan found herself asking, dully. The dullness was a plea, and it stopped Helen in her tracks.

The reply was gentle. 'The children are up early.

You don't have to stay up all——'

Devan's smile came, quick and flashing. 'Well,' she said brightly, cutting her sister off in mid-sentence, 'I'll see you tomorrow, then.'

Helen just stopped and smiled. 'OK,' she said quietly, and then she paused before leaving. 'Oh, yes, don't forget the book you left on the picnic table this morning.'

'I'll go and get it now,' Devan promised, and then Helen was gone.

She sighed, and glanced at the cat to make sure he was still busy with his food, and then she went out of the back door. The screen banged behind her, yellow rectangle in warm scented evening, and as she approached the picnic bench, which was battered and peeling from years of outside weathering and use, she nearly leaped from the confines of her skin when a strange masculine voice said quietly, 'Lady, you are one hell of a person to get in touch with.'

Somewhat surprised to find herself still intact after that shock, Devan took a few more steps forward, which brought her to the shadows of the large maple, under which the picnic bench sat. On it was the dark form of a man, and her mind took that just-heard voice and clicked it smoothly with her image of the afternoon's visitor. How tenacious can you get? she thought, mildly. She could see her book, a hardback, lying not quite as she'd left it. He must have riffled through it. 'Perhaps,' she said drily, reaching over and picking it up, 'that's because I don't wish to be reached.'

She turned back to her bright yellow rectangle. His voice came, still quietly. 'Why did you lie earlier?'

No anger in him. She let her feet shuffle to stillness as his question hung in the air for her to answer. If he had done to her what she had done to him, she'd be furious. She opened her mouth, hesitated, and turned her head to the side to hear if he moved. 'I don't know,' she said, and started to leave again.

His voice stopped her a second time. 'Why are you lying now?'

That finally brought her around, and she tried to pick out his features in the dark. 'Who the hell are you, anyway?'

He was replying almost before she'd finished, with a quickening of tone that finally revealed his frustration. 'Isn't it about time you asked that, instead of running blindly away again?'

A moment of silence. She stared at the shadow where he sat, and had, apparently, been sitting all day. Then she said, rather slowly, as she looked down at the book she held, 'I was just wishing I hadn't. We heard you leave.'

'To change into dry clothes,' he said, his voice wry. 'I was waiting here when your sister and her son came back. She told me that if you didn't want to see me, I'd have a long wait.' Devan didn't know why she was shocked by that, but she was. She suddenly realised that Helen had sent her outside purposely, on the off-chance this stranger was still waiting for her.

'She was right,' she retorted, backing a step.

'I'm Ryan Forrester,' said the man simply. Third shock of the night, only this was by far the worst; this was nightmarish, this was a confrontation she couldn't face. Then he said, almost gently, 'Devan, surely you didn't believe that I wouldn't come?'

Him! She knew him. She knew his signature, his caustic wit, his keen observations, his crystal-clear thinking. She knew his dispassionate support, his criticisms, his distant interest. She knew him but had never met him in person, never before this, and this was too late. Without warning, she turned and raced hard back for the house. She had the advantage of surprise, she could do it, she'd reach the inside of the kitchen, slam and lock the door on him, and she wouldn't see him again. Ever.

Not if she had anything to say about it. But though he had been on the other side of the picnic bench and seated, though she was fast and in fair physical shape, though by her calculations she should have made it, she didn't, for a sudden whirlwind rush came up behind her, and his hands shot out, grabbing her arms, whirling her none too gently around.

She dropped her book and listened to it slap on to the grassy ground. She stared up at him, her mouth a distorted ugly line of bitterness, upheaval and defeat crashing in on her in waves, her straight, shoulder-length hair blown about and wild. The light from the kitchen fell on him fully, and it was the first clear look she'd ever had of him. His determined, forceful features, those grey-blue eyes looking pinpointed with black, that deep, puzzled frown between his level brows—he stood out from the blackness behind him in sharp relief, everything down to the column of his throat and the open-necked shirt he wore so casually.

Her wild and erratic heartbeat must be palpable to him, he held her so tightly. He looked shocked, half angry too. 'Why,' he breathed, nearly crushing her between his big hands without even realising it, 'why did you run at the sound of my name? We've been corresponding for three years! I thought we'd established something, a sort of trust. Haven't I been a fair editor to you? Haven't I   '

Confusion teemed in Devan at this onslaught of near accusation. She bent her head and thrust her hands into her hair, mouth opening, breathing deep for a moment. She felt a surge of heat rush through her, leaving her cold and shaken. 'Hold on a minute,' she grated, and then pulled free of his warm, strong hands. Better now; he wasn't touching her, and she was unfettered, could think clearer. 'I never said any of this was you. In fact, I never said anything at all. Just drop this, go away, and leave me alone, all right?'

She had sounded really good, and was quite proud of herself, until the very end when her voice had begun to tremble in a horribly revealing manner. He was standing right where she'd left him, his arms hanging at his sides, the hands still. 'No,' he said incredulously. 'No, I won't go away. This is our first meeting in three years of working together and you slam your door in my face and tell me to get lost? This isn't like you! This isn't the dynamic, open person that's written so many letters to me! No, it's not all right!' Half turned away from him yet unable to walk away, she watched as he dug his right hand into his pocket and dragged out something white, holding it in his fist like a weapon. 'I want to know what the hell this last letter you wrote to me meant! I've spent practically six months tracking you down to some godforsaken backwood——'

He wasn't supposed to take it this way; he wasn't supposed to be like this—puzzled, angry, so damned concerned she could sense it vibrating from him tangibly; he wasn't supposed to be so vital. She had the sensation that she was drowning, overwhelmed, for this was too much to take. Devan silently bowed her head and put one of her hands over her eyes, as harshly exposed in the bright light and deep darkness as he had been. At thirty, she was a thin woman, now too thin, and her arm and hand showed like a stark stick, barely able to support the weary, eloquent defeat of her bent head.

His flow of words stopped in mid-sentence. He stared and he stared, and she knew it because she had lifted her head at his silence and saw. He was standing very still, as if trying to absorb something that was totally unexpected, totally shocking. 'My God!' he said then, sounding tired. 'What's happened to you?'

CHAPTER TWO

DEVAN'S hand dropped to her side. She lifted her face and felt the faintest stirring of breezes touch at her skin as though in benediction. Then she turned and bent to pick up her book, moving carefully, moving like an old woman. 'Now that you've come all this way,' she said flatly, accepting at last that this was a meeting she could no longer avoid, 'You might as well come in and have a cup of coffee.'

Ryan Forrester sighed, the sound rising in a gentle swell over the distant sound of summer breeze, and then, as she started slowly back to the house, he silently followed. At the screen door, she glanced to the floor and saw the tomcat stretched, from front paws to back paws, right across the doorway like a mat. It was his favourite position after a meal, and he would lie, eyes slitted, ears lazily laid back, as he listened to the sounds from outdoors wafting through the fine metal mesh of the screen. She opened the door and carefully avoided him, and then threw over her shoulder, 'Don't step on Paris.'

'What?' asked Ryan Forrester blankly, just behind her.

She turned her head. Their eyes met briefly. 'The cat. Don't step on him.'

For the first time he looked down, and then his

expression changed, turned wry. 'OK,' he said, and carefully stepped over the immobile cat.

Devan walked calmly over to the cupboard and dragged down another cup. She went to the coffee maker, a battered, much used model, and poured hot liquid into the cups and then she turned. Ryan was standing quietly by the kitchen table, his quick, observant eyes running over the light green curtains, the print tiled floor, the scarred worktops. Her eyebrows went up in polite enquiry, and he looked at her when she asked, 'Do you take anything in yours?'

His grey-blue eyes searched her features quickly, trying to learn to read her expression. A strange face with a familiar personality. He was trying, she realised, to understand her as quickly as possible, and her mouth turned in a self-mocking twist. He said quietly, 'Nothing, thank you.'

She handed him his coffee, and then went to sit in a kitchen chair opposite him, sipping at her cup with a blank face and eyes. The sooner he could understand her, the sooner he could rectify the situation he thought she was in, and things could get back to normal. Anger shuddered through her in a storm. Such unknowing arrogance. 'How did you track me down?' she asked conversationally.

She watched as a faint, wry smile touched at his well-cut lips and then faded, and he reached out a big corded hand to draw out a nearby chair and sink into it. He bent his head, blond hairs lighting in his light brown hair, and he drank at the strong, undiluted coffee and then visibly shuddered. He set the cup down very carefully, looked at her black coffee as though it were poison, and asked as if he couldn't help himself, 'You actually enjoy drinking that?'

'I'm an addict,' she said, deadpan calm. She raised her cup deliberately and drank more.

Something briefly dark flickered in those light eyes. Then he leaned his arms on the table in front of him and said evenly, 'First I checked all the leads I possibly could, from your past letters, your former address, your neighbours. Then, in desperation, I went to your bank and told the manager our firm had made a mistake in royalty payments by depositing far too much in your account. When he checked your account file, I stole a peek at it and saw this address.'

Her lips unwillingly tugged into a quick, amused smile. 'That's very illegal,' she told him.

Paris twitched, and rolled on to his back, his paws dangling in the air. Ryan said quietly, his eyes holding hers, 'By then I didn't care.'

Inside, the light was more gentle on her features and her body lines. She sat at her ease, leaning her elbow on the table while resting her chin in her hand, the fingers carelessly curled halfway over her mouth. Her dark hair was still tousled and untidy, and she felt and showed a supreme indifference to the fact, which somehow made the blown hair very attractive. It was glossy, framing a finely featured face, with delicately shaped lips and nose, and a strong brow over utterly weary eyes. The eyes were what Ryan looked at, those brown, patient, calm, studying eyes of hers, for at the back of their expression was a blackness.

He moved suddenly, shifting in his chair, sitting forward, laying his hand down on the table with a slap, his eyes burning. 'I didn't care,' he said, low and hard, 'because at first, sure, you'd bothered me with that last letter. But I thought you just needed a break, time to get away and think. And then I didn't hear from you. For months I waited and I didn't hear a damned thing from you and I got scared. I came to see if you were all right.'

His voice had gone flat, and in the silence that followed his words she knew he was waiting, waiting to hear something from her; anything, words of reassurance, words of denial—words. She didn't have any to give him. She looked down at her cup and brooded almost dispassionately. She didn't have any to give any more.

Ryan thrust the last letter she had sent to him under her nose and shook it. It was creased, and half crumpled in his grip. 'What does this mean?' he asked urgently, trying to shake her with his voice, yet trying to keep his frustration in control. 'For the last three years you've been so full of brilliance and fire, and burning ambition! Every letter you've ever sent me has practically vibrated off my desk with the power and conviction of your vitality, and then, out of the blue, I get this quiet, subdued letter of farewell. What does it *mean*?'

She gave a little laugh that wasn't a laugh at all, as her eyes met his, and flared briefly to life. 'It means that I quit,' she said lightly. 'I had thought

I'd made myself perfectly clear in it; perhaps I've lost that ability, too.'

'You can't quit!' he said passionately.

She thrust away from the table at that, and dragged her cup along with her. Then, with jerky, uncoordinated movements, she went to the coffee maker and poured herself another cup. As an afterthought, she reached below the worktop, pulled out her bottle of Christian Brother's brandy, and splashed a careless dollop into the cup. She leaned against the worktop, turned to face him, and took a burning gulp. 'Why not?' she asked, flippantly, crossing her ankles. 'Because I didn't fulfil my contract? Be assured that if I'm not writing for you, I'm certainly not writing for anyone else.'

Her eyes, hard brown pebbles, stared into his as he drew in a swift, audible breath at that. Then anger darkened his face. He virtually flushed from it, standing up so violently he sent his chair back a few feet. 'You can't quit!' he said again. He was so obtuse, she couldn't believe it, and she put her back to him so that he could flay her raw with what she knew he was going to say. 'You're meteoric, you're better than good, you're only thirty years old and you've written four bestsellers—you're a future Pulitzer candidate, damn it! Devan Richardson, what are you afraid of? Is it success?'

That sent her to laughing again, lightly, liltingly, and it pealed off into the stunned silence behind her. 'Ah, yes,' she said then, bitingly, bitterly. She took her cup and drained the liquid in one go, burning her throat with liquor and hot coffee, feeling the drink explode in her stomach and radiate warmth. 'That's rich, that is! I finish college in three years; I bust my butt as a reporter for the next four while I write at night. I get five rejections on my first manuscript so I rewrite the damned thing and send it to you, and before you've given me an answer on it, I send you my second!' She turned to him then, taut, angry; futile and angry. 'I worked stints of ten days in a row, twelve hours a day.' Her voice went raw. 'You jackass, does that sound like I'm afraid of success?'

Eyes dilated, he said shortly, 'No, it doesn't. It was a stupid thing to say. But if not that, then what? Why?'

As suddenly as she had flared up, she calmed down, turning as if at random to survey the kitchen worktop which was neat and bare, except for cannisters of flour and sugar, the coffee maker, and now the brandy bottle. She poured herself a third cup, this time fully half brandy, and then turned to hand the bottle to him without a word. He reached for it slowly, his eyes steady on her, and then he poured a substantial dollop into his cup and screwed the lid back on. She swirled the liquid in her cup around, staring at it while she wondered if Helen was in bed asleep or not. She smelled the pungent liquor and, as suddenly as she'd poured it, she set it down with a sharp clatter and left it abandoned on the counter, walking to sit heavily in her chair again.

'For,' she said softly, looking at her slim hands,

'a very simple reason. I've lost it. There's nothing to write any more. I haven't anything to say.' She watched her wristwatch, a birthday present from Helen, wink in the light. 'I don't know, maybe I pushed too hard. Maybe I was too ambitious. I—used to walk away from my typewriter so damned tired I could hardly see straight. I was on fire; I knew just where I was going and how to get there.' Her lips pulled into a faint smile, as her voice mocked herself. 'Ah, I *knew* I was good! Every word I put on a white page was magic, gold in my fingertips. I had so many themes, meanings and images crowding me, I didn't know what to write first.' A pause, while he waited with a statue's stillness, this stranger, this friend, this man whose insight she knew, and absolutely nothing else. She rubbed at her full bottom lip with her index finger, slowly, staring with blind eyes into nothing. 'I've lost it,' she said again, simply.

He came forward swiftly, and sat as he said reassuringly, 'No need to panic, Devan. You've just got a writer's block. People get them from time to time—they're damned upsetting, they're scary, they're unpredictable. But sooner or later, they go away.'

She turned her eyes to him, focusing on his face with those direct, light, compelling eyes; the frowning sincerity, his grim assurance. She smiled faintly and said, 'No.'

'How can you say that?' he shot back, very fast. 'Have you ever experienced one before?'

Those wide shoulders leaning forward, that big

hand clenched into a fist on the table. She closed her eyes as she felt the pain pricking at the back of them. 'You still don't understand,' she whispered. 'This isn't a block. It's a burn-out.'

She felt against her sensitive lip her pulse beating in the end of her finger, one, two. Paris shook his head with flattened ears and then laid it back down again, to sigh gustily. Moths, attracted to the interior light, bashed senselessly against the screen of the back door, white fluttering specks against black. 'You pushed yourself to exhaustion,' said Ryan then, persistently. 'Give yourself time. Take life easy! Then, when you've got a new perspective on things——'

She slammed both hands down on the table so hard, she felt pain in her shoulders, and she cried out, '*I've given myself a goddamned year*!' His facial features clenched together with the pain in her outburst, raw and throbbing; her pain was always raw. Distantly she registered quick, light footsteps on the stairs. 'Ryan Forrester,' she then said, savagely, through her teeth, 'do you have any idea how long a year is? Do you have any idea how many times I've gone to the typewriter to sit and try to get the words to flow? Do you know what it's like to live, day in, day out, trying to keep busy, trying to patch your life together for just a little longer, trying to have faith and hold on to anything, any hope, any glimmering of an idea, anything at all that will keep you sane and help you to believe in the future? I do. I don't have any more faith.'

Rawness like bared, wounded flesh; raw despair. She had to laugh inwardly, bitterly, at herself. She had had the fine idea of keeping herself aloof, distant from her past. Then along trots her editor and she spills her guts out, all over the table. No dignity at all in that!

Helen's voice came tentatively from the doorway, worriedly, as she looked at the two in the kitchen. 'Devan?'

They both ignored her. And if Devan had thought she had felt pain before, if she had thought she was in pain now, she must have been mistaken, for it was as nothing compared to what he made her feel when he said then, with great gentleness, 'I do.'

She said, before she could help it, 'I bet you go to church, too.'

She drew in a swift breath, appalled at herself, and then he said with an audible thread of amusement, 'Sometimes, yes.'

She turned her head to the side, and saw Helen still hovering in the doorway, wrapped to the throat in her dressing-gown. She said to Ryan, 'Finish your coffee.'

At that he went to the sink and dumped his cup. 'That,' he said succinctly, 'is an impossibility. Even with the brandy, that brew tasted like sin.' He'd meant to make her smile, but she didn't have it in her, and after a moment he turned to the doorway and acknowledged Helen's presence with a smile of his own, and a nod. 'Hello, again. I'm Ryan Forrester, Devan's editor.'

Helen regarded him with great respect. 'You were still outside waiting, then?' she said. 'I hadn't really expected you to last that long.'

Devan said between her teeth, 'Full points for persistence.' Her sister sent her a reproachful look, but Ryan just smiled.

He flipped up his watch to check the time and then said, with a sigh, 'Look, it's very late. If you'll excuse me for saying so, you look like death.' Her shoulders shook once in a reluctant, silent chuckle, and his eyes sharpened on her. 'May I come over tomorrow morning?'

At that Devan's eyes flashed brief and brilliant at him, making his eyes widen and his expression become arrested, but the brilliance and the flash were transitory and her eyes died to dull brown. 'For what?' she asked flippantly, remembering her drink, by now quite cold. She went to get it, drinking it for the alcohol, drinking it like a person who needs it very badly. The confrontation was taking more out of her than she cared to admit. Then she wiped her lips with fingers that visibly trembled, and said, 'Not more of this post mortem, surely?'

His nostrils flared, and his head reared back. But whatever he might have said was lost, for he shook himself loose of whatever emotion she had prompted in him and said very softly, 'I don't believe in post mortems.'

She bowed her head and turned her face away, in rejection of everything she saw in him. 'We have nothing to discuss,' she said, coldly.

He bared his teeth in something not quite a smile, and said between them, 'Like hell, lady!' Her hands tightened on her cup, but she refused to look at him. 'Somebody needs to take this in hand.'

And then, unexpectedly, Helen deserted Devan to walk over to Ryan and hold out her hand with a friendly smile. As she shook his hand, she said, 'I'm Devan's sister, and I couldn't agree with you more, Mr Forrester. You'll be more than welcome to come any time you like.'

Aghast at this treachery, Devan glared at her calm sister with an open mouth, and then she shut her jaws with a snap. Her expression grew ominous, and she said very softly, 'Helen Marie Beardley, you have just made a grave tactical error, and if you think this is the end of it, you're sadly mistaken——'

'Well, then,' said Ryan, briskly. He clasped Helen's hand once more and then let her go, and he strode for the back door. He threw over his wide, capable-looking shoulder, 'I'll be here at nine, sharp. Don't bother locking your doors or shuttering your windows. I know you'll be here.' At the door, he stopped and turned to consider her, standing tense and defensive at the worktop. Then he said, sweetly, 'Nice meeting you, Devan, Helen. I'll be seeing you.'

He was gone, sending Paris leaping out of his way. The cat streaked towards the front of the house, and Devan and Helen were left staring at the empty black rectangle that was the screen door. Empty, black; and Devan caught herself almost believing, almost hoping. She shook her head savagely, forcing herself to remember past failures, past disappointments.

She rounded on Helen with a near shriek. 'How could you do that? Couldn't you see that I didn't want him around? For God's sake, Helen, this is the last thing I need!'

'I think you're wrong,' said her sister, quietly. Devan dropped her face to her hands. 'You see, I've given you what peace and support that I can, but it isn't enough.'

'It is, too!' The words were muffled against her palms.

'No,' Helen said gently. 'Because you're stagnating here, my dear. You and I—we're two different personalities. You may enjoy the placidity and serenity of our lives right now, but you need a dynamic stimulus to push you out of the rut you're in. And while I love you, and though you will always be welcome in my house, I know you enough to realise I can't give you what you need.' Devan's hands dropped, and her head rose slowly to stare at her sister's calm, loving smile. 'Good night, love.'

The kitchen was empty. Devan stared blindly at the screen door. Ryan Forester, out of her past, a faceless name with a cutting mind. And she didn't know a thing of his motivations, his emotions, his goals or dreams. Ryan Forrester, total stranger. She drained her cup then, with a gulp, and then shook with a fit of coughing as the spirit went down wrong. With a sudden welling rage, she took the cup's handle in her right hand and threw it with all her force at that black rectangle, both watching and hearing it shatter, the pieces flying in a deadly ricochet. Her breath dragged into her lungs with something terribly close to a sob. After a long, long moment, she pulled away from the worktop and began cleaning up the mess. On her hands and knees by the door, wiping methodically with a wet cloth to pick up the fragments, she let her head sink to her hands while her face broke into a soundless, wordless, formless expression of anguish.

If only it were as simple as Ryan and Helen believed! If only it were a question of sitting back and waiting, as he'd suggested. But then Ryan thought he understood the situation, whereas she knew that he most certainly did not. No, by God, he didn't know the half of it. But don't, Devan, don't think back. Don't think.

Don't feel. Don't feel. Don't feel.

CHAPTER THREE

SHE fell into her bed ten minutes later with an eagerness that surprised her. Devan, the original night owl, crawling like a wreck under her covers at barely eleven o'clock. Three, four o'clock in the morning—even dawn was no stranger to her. Once she would have looked up in surprise to note the time which had flown by swiftly with the hot pace of her work. Now she couldn't believe how long, how slowly, how excruciatingly the time ticked by.

But not this night. She felt dizzy before she even sank into a lying position. The buzz she had got from the combined caffeine and alcohol was making the world whirl. When she laid her head down, she knew that this of all nights would not be sleepless.

She awoke to cheery birds singing, interspersed with a loud and insistent knocking. Knocking that sounded rhythmic as if it had gone on for some time. Knocking that brought her to full alertness, as she dragged herself out of bed and threw on her bathrobe to pad down the stairs in bare feet. Knocking that didn't stop, even as she made her way to the front door. She yanked it open and glared with dry, itchy eyes at Ryan Forrester who leaned against the doorpost, elegantly dressed, neatly shaved and wide awake.

She briefly checked her wristwatch, which she had plucked from atop her dresser on her way out of her bedroom, and she said shortly, 'Nine o'clock! Good for you, dead on time, damn you. Excuse me.' She turned around, looking and feeling like a mess, feeling unable to face the sunshine and this man, this day. She said through a yawn, 'Help yourself to whatever you like.'

'Where's your sister?' he asked, coming slowly into the house.

'Dunno.' She started for the stairs.

'Where are you going?' He followed her.

'Back to bed.' She started up the staircase, her eyes looking up their length in dull desperation. Sleep. She felt as if she could sleep for a month. Another wide yawn cracked her jaws. She'd sure as hell give it a try.

His hand was on her arm then, stopping her. 'No, you're not,' he said quietly. She turned very calmly and stared him in the eye, her hair tousled even more than the night before, her expression weary, her eyes wryly resigned.

'Look,' she said politely, removing his hand with her own. For a brief moment she felt warm skin, corded strength, long fingers. 'You are a very nice man. I don't even dislike you after yesterday. You were a wonderfully supportive, intelligent, and, yes, fair editor to me, so thanks a lot. But this is my life, and it's no concern of yours, so go back to your own and quit meddling in affairs that don't concern you, all right?' He just regarded her with those light, unreadable eyes. She reached up an insolent hand and patted his cheek. 'There's a good boy. Lock the door when you leave.' She started up the stairs again, hearing nothing behind her, no retreat, no outburst, though she had seen quick and dangerous anger flare in his face when she had patted him. Absolutely nothing. It impelled her to turn around again, to stare down at him standing motionless and staring up at her, his expression blank. She said, as if goaded, 'You're not wanted here!'

And then Devan made her way to her bedroom, not caring. Not caring if he ransacked the house, came up the stairs and stole from under their noses, not caring if he took every single stick of furniture she and Helen owned. She dropped her bathrobe to the floor and climbed into bed, falling on her pillow like a heavy stone, closing her eyes and pulling the covers over her head. Not caring.

Ryan stood at the bottom of the stairs for several moments after she had disappeared, staring up at the empty, shadowed hall. He looked around, noting the rather odd combination of cleanliness and disaster that was the ground floor, littered with toys. His brows rose, mildly. Then, through the open archway that led to the dining room, he spotted a white square of paper. He went to it, curiously.

For a few moments, Devan felt the smoothness and the warmth of her bed, her pillow lying soft and yielding underneath her head, silence reigning through the house. Then she heard a few slight, far-off sounds of someone moving through the downstairs rooms, but they were too faint for her to guess what was happening. Until, out of the clear, sunny quiet exploded the unmistakable, heady strains of 'Jesus Christ Superstar'. Devan bolted upright in her bed as though she'd lain on hot bricks, her glossy hair swirling about her face. She panted once, twice, with the shock of it, then blinked. Her album! He was playing her album at top volume, loud enough to wake the dead! She flung her covers off, and they slid to the floor. Then she was off the mattress in a bound, and striding for her wardrobe door, which she ripped open. The door hit the wall and came back to slap her shoulder. She dragged on faded, ancient jeans and a sweater, not bothering with a bra or socks and shoes, dressing as swiftly as possible so she could run down the stairs and confront that strange and infuriating man who was apparently intent on disrupting her life.

Her step faltered for a brief, telling moment as she thought of that. Such as her life was. But then she had recovered and was racing down the steps, taking them three at a time and landing in the hallway with a jar she felt to her teeth. She strode for the open doorway of one of the rooms she'd converted to a library, the one which held her stereo. Ryan was nonchalantly lounging in an armchair and blandly smiled when she appeared in the doorway.

She screamed at him, 'What, in God's name, do you think you're doing?' His brows rose slowly, and she took the distance from the doorway to the stereo in long paces. Without a thought for the record, she ripped the needle off it, which made the speakers shriek, and then she slapped the arm on the rest.

When she whirled to face him again, he said mildly, 'You did say I should help myself to whatever I like.'

She stood there, opening and shutting her mouth like a gasping fish. Then she thrust her hand through her hair, and looked around. 'Where the hell is Helen, anyway? Where are the kids?'

He held up a scrap of paper. 'She left this on the dining room table. She took the children shopping for the morning so that we could have a little privacy.'

Devan's jaw spasmodically bunched. She could well understand why Helen had done so. Her sister had most probably guessed, and rightly, that sparks would fly this morning, and she was removing the children from the scene. Devan got a grim hold of her teeming emotions, and then smiled pleasantly. 'How old are you?' she asked.

He had faced her calmly, even cheerfully, but he most certainly had not been expecting that. His brows shot up in astonishment as he took in her bland face and the brown eyes that were glittering hard and bright with rage. Then he smiled, in genuine amusement. 'I'm thirty-nine,' he told her, placidly. She cocked her head briefly at that.

'So young, to be chief editor for a major publishing firm,' she said, admiringly. Then her expression lost all pleasantness and became a vivid, tight indication of her anger. 'But you're a big boy now, and you know what it means when someone says no, don't you? But you don't listen, do you? Well, you'd better listen to this, mister. Get the hell out of this house, or I'm calling the police.'

He looked around, as if seeing everything for the first time. 'But this isn't your home,' he said simply.

Quietly. Nothing he had said had been in a loud or raised voice; everything had been said so very quietly. She actually, physically, felt the blood leave her face at what he had said, felt it drain away until she was dizzy and white. A year she had lived here and tried to fit into a different way of life, with different expectations, and quietly he had managed to reach right to the truth with his observations and his words. His light eyes were watching her intently, with some surprise, for her reaction, and she saw him tense. Only later did she realise that he had expected her to faint.

She found her voice, and it trembled. 'Don't you have a job and responsibilities? Don't you have somewhere better to be? Don't you have things to do, places to go, people to meet? For God's sake, go away and leave me alone!'

His eyes were widened in that lean, mature face, and they were recording everything about her. His feet were planted wide apart as though he meant to stay and there could be no doubt of it. Then he said, lightly, 'Why, so you can drown in your self-pity?'

She felt how badly her composure had slipped when her face showed how stunned she was at that. 'You bastard,' she said, through thinned white lips. 'What do you know about what I'm drowning in?'

He returned, swiftly and compellingly, 'If not self-pity, then tell me what.'

Comprehension dawned in her eyes and she nodded slowly once. Then she said, almost viciously, 'Oh, no you don't.' And she turned to stalk out of the room.

She was making for the kitchen, and a terrible, shaking impotence filled her as he followed closely on her heels. He whipped her around with one hand and said angrily, 'What the hell did that mean?'

She stabbed the air between them with her forefinger, refusing to back down. 'I know what you're trying to do!' she accused, and he looked more surprised than ever. 'You're trying to goad me, aren't you?'

'I'm trying to understand you!' he shouted, and the sound of his raised voice shocked her into silence. 'Why in the world would I want to goad you?'

'I don't know! Maybe you're trying to get me to make some great confession that will cleanse my soul, but let me tell you, mister, it's not going to work!'

'Aren't you making a few assumptions here?' he snapped, his eyes sparkling black and hot dia-mond-blue. His face was etched with his own anger, and Devan blinked at the sight of those

forceful, hardened features, feeling herself lose
ground. 'I never said I wanted to listen to any
confession!'

'Then what are you doing here?' she shot back,
and his eyes flickered. The back door opened then,
and they both whirled round as if struck to see
Helen, Janie and Gary trudge indoors.

'You're back,' said Janie, looking Ryan up and
down with frank curiosity.

Helen, also, was looking from Ryan to Devan,
thoughtfully, and she noted the anger still flushed
in both faces. 'I take it,' she said calmly, 'that we
came back too early?'

Devan threw up her hands in defeat and said
disgustedly, as though in answer to Helen's
question, 'I can't get rid of him!' Gary was sticking
his tongue through the gap in his front teeth while
he scratched at his ear. Devan jerked her arm out
of Ryan's loose grip and stormed out of the house.

Barefoot, she swept across the back yard and
down a short path that led to a small clearing.
There, feeling at least as if she'd managed to put
some distance between herself and the scene she'd
just had with Ryan Forrester, she threw herself
down on the ground and stretched flat. Her
heartbeat was racing wildly, and she put a hand to
her chest in wonder. She hadn't been so upset in
what seemed like ages, and she was amazed at her
own reaction to Ryan's persistence.

She stared up to the leafy-laced blue sky, and
while her eyes traced the overhead tangle of
branches, she forced herself to take deep, calming

lungfuls of air. White clouds scuttled across the visible blue. Slowly she began to relax. Everything seemed so crazy. Everything was so tangled, like the canopy of branches that was shading her from the sun.

Him. Where had he come from, why did he upset her so? Why did he have to stick his nose into her affairs, and thrust his vital, sincere, masculine presence on her? Why was she so affected by him? Was it just because he reminded her of one of the most painful times in her life? Her face broke into a frustrated sob before righting again. Why wouldn't he leave her be?

The bright blue and green swaying branches above her blurred as she blinked several times, feeling how heavy her eyelids were. She was so exhausted. The one time she would have slept, and someone had to come along and play rock opera. In spite of herself, before her eyes closed one last time, she had to grin as she thought of the crashing strains of music, and her own panting shock. He had nerve, she'd give him that.

The wind rustled restlessly through the surrounding trees and foliage. It muffled the sounds of Ryan's approach, and he stood at the edge of the clearing for several minutes, looking his fill of the sleeping, slim figure now curled into a foetal position. Devan had tucked her arm under her head in her sleep, and the wind stirred her hair, blowing it across her face. Her expression was softened, vulnerable, exhausted. Then, very quietly, Ryan retraced his steps and entered the kitchen, where Helen was preparing lunch for Janie and Gary.

'She's asleep,' he said quietly, as he took the seat Helen offered to him.

'I'm not surprised,' said Helen, and she placed sandwiches in front of the two children, who fell on them like ravenous wolves. 'Please join us for lunch. You're more than welcome.'

He hesitated, met her frank and friendly eyes, and then smiled. 'I'd love to, thank you.' He watched her for a few moments while she deftly made more sandwiches, and then he asked curiously, 'Why aren't you surprised, if I might ask? I mean, why would you have expected that reaction, as opposed to another?'

'It was rather inevitable, actually,' said Devan's sister, as she sat down to the meal she had prepared. 'You see, Devan doesn't do a whole lot of eating or sleeping. She's been creeping around this last year with about as much vitality as a wraith.'

His brows, light brown and sleek, rose in surprise at that. 'Do you mean she isn't always so volatile?'

'Oh, she used to be. That kind of personality takes a lot of energy to maintain, though, and after last night and this morning, she must be feeling pretty drained.' Helen turned her attention to her son, who was systematically punching his half-eaten sandwich full of finger holes. 'Gary, stop that.'

Ryan was mulling over what Helen had said while he ate the sandwiches she had prepared for him. 'What caused such a change in her?' he asked then.

Helen just smiled gently. 'I don't really think I'm in the position to be talking of Devan's private life without her consent, do you, Mr Forrester?'

After a moment, he smiled back and said, 'Call me Ryan.'

'Yah!'

The bloodcurdling yell resounded through the forest and brought Devan to wakefulness with a shriek of her own. Then, from nowhere, a body landed heavily on her unprotected stomach, and she felt the breath go out of her with a whuff! Her glazed eyes swivelled wildly to stare at Gary's triumphant, fierce expression. He stuck his grubby hand into her wind-tangled hair and then used a knobby stick to saw at it, and he leaped away before Devan had time to gather her wits about her.

'I got your scalp!' he shouted, gleefully blood-thirsty. She sat dazedly, and then thrust herself to her feet. He danced just beyond her reach.

'You!' she panted, fulminatingly.

'Yah, yah! I got your scalp!'

She started to march his way, slow and determined. He began to edge back as she looked at his empty, clenched fist and said grimly, 'Give it back.'

He laughed with delight, a quicksilver, tow-headed urchin with pure devilry looking out of his eyes. 'No way!' he shouted, waving his fist. 'It's mine! Yah, got your scalp, got your scalp! You're a bald egg!'

Devan had to grin herself, and she said chillingly between her teeth in response, 'And you are one dead kid.' His eyes grew wide with sparkling apprehension, and then he whirled and ran.

She pelted after his fleet figure as best she could in her bare feet, and the two raced across the lawn. He was screaming the whole way, and she was yelling a fierce reply, but couldn't seem to catch up with him, and then he smashed through the back screen door and it slammed shut behind him.

Devan hit it full tilt and stopped with a painful, abrupt grunt. Gary was just on the other side, a shadowy figure out of the sunlight. She tried the handle of the door to make sure, and there was no doubt about it; he had definitely locked her out. 'Gary,' she said, with a dangerous sweetness. 'You are cheating. Now, unlock the door.'

'Yah, got your scalp!'

'You are a repulsive little monster who doesn't play fair,' she said calmly, which didn't bother him in the slightest. 'And I quit if you are going to act like this. Now, open the door so I can come inside.'

Splash!

A cascade of water exploded on Devan's head and shoulders, and she stood in utter, complete, unbreathing immobility for three full seconds, her eyes screwed tightly shut in reflex, her shoulders hunched and her mouth open. Then her head hung, sagging from her neck in shock. She raised dripping hands and rubbed at her eyes, and then lifted her head again to peer at the upper-storey window. They had indeed set a brilliant trap, those ruthless two. Janie was hanging out, her carrot head shaking with merriment, the plastic bucket dangling from one slim freckled hand.

She could hear Gary whooping his own satisfaction, and then light footsteps clicked across the kitchen floor and Helen unlocked the screen door to peer up calmly at her daughter. By then Devan was breathing again, and she mopped her streaming hair off her face to say bitterly, 'You, madam, did not give birth to humans. You spawned devils.'

Her sister didn't turn a hair at this accusation. 'You have only yourself to blame,' she suggested reasonably, 'since they learnt it from you.'

Devan squinted up again at the imp above her. She couldn't hold her own laughter back and was giggling as insanely as either of the two children. She pointed to Janie and warned darkly, 'You realise, of course, that I'm going to get both of you for this.'

But threats couldn't cloud Janie's victory as she was now well removed from Devan's reach, so she stuck out her tongue impudently before her head abruptly disappeared. Now free to enter, Devan stepped into the house while mopping at her brow with the soaking sleeve of her sweater. She would have to go upstairs to change, but was in no hurry as she was quite sure that both her niece and nephew would be well out of range by now. She would get no retaliation easily on that pair.

Her eyes were getting used to the darker interior of the house just at the same time as she was realising from whom a low, attractive masculine laugh was emanating. She glanced over to the table and involuntarily grinned as she took in Ryan, sitting with his face buried in one huge hand while his wide shoulders shook.

'I might have known you'd enjoy that,' she said drily, without heat.

His hand lowered and his brilliant laughing eyes met hers. Her own were dancing with amusement, and her expression was open and unguarded for the first time since he'd met her face to face. But then a kind of shock bolted though her at the sight of him, his hard face vivid, alight, his long body curled in indolent ease at the table. He must have been feeling something quite similar, for his eyes widened at her expression, and the laughter was dying from his face to leave him looking rather thoughtful.

She jerked through the room. 'I'd better change,' she said shortly, and she raced up the stairs.

In the privacy of her room, she savagely towelled her hair dry and then combed it, and she changed into dry jeans and a sweater. She briefly thought about putting on socks and shoes but couldn't find a good reason to, so she didn't. She was beginning to feel distinctly shaky, so she headed down for the kitchen again, and made straight for the worktop to make a full pot of coffee; she stopped stock still when she saw no coffee maker sitting in the

accustomed place. After a moment, so full of
outrage and something else, something strange at
this continual, damnable interfering, she said very
softly, 'All right. Where is it?'

She swivelled on her bare heel to glare at both
Helen and Ryan. Helen gave a sigh. Ryan said
courteously, 'I locked it in my car boot, along with
the coffee grounds, the tea, and the liquor.' A tidal
wave of fury swamped her with such intensity, she
barely held back the impulse to raise her arm and
strike him. Their eyes met, and she could see that
he had expected no less, and was waiting for it. He
hadn't so much as flinched.

She turned instead to her sister and spat, 'How
could you?'

Helen looked at the table, and sighed. 'I didn't
have anything to do with it,' she said.

'You could have stopped him.' The words were
measured, spaced for emphasis.

Her sister looked her full in the eyes then and
said gently, 'I know. But I happen to think he's
right.' Her eyes went to Ryan, then back to
Devan's, and she said quietly, 'Excuse me.'

Devan listened to her leave, feeling utterly
deserted, and then she turned to her persecutor.
'You,' she said with great feeling, 'are going to be
the death of me, yet. Do you really expect me to put
up with this?'

'Yes,' he said simply, with a singularly sweet
smile on his determined, masculine features.
Shock upon shock, and she was swamped with
something else, a sensory overload, this stranger

having wrung her through the emotional wringer in a night and a day. She stood there quietly, no less angry for her quietness, which was a manifestation of her busy thinking. He was regarding her with great interest. In the light of day, his light blue-grey eyes were striking against his deep tan. He was asking, while watching her with those alert eyes, 'This morning, was there something you might have had to tell me, had I goaded you? Is there something more to this—problem than a mere block—all right, burn-out, or whatever the hell you'd like to call it?'

She was suddenly tired again, and shaking with it. She put down her head to rub at her forehead with one of her long, slim hands. 'It won't work,' she said softly. 'Whatever method you choose to use, it's not going to work.' All emotion had drained away, all of the bright amusement, friendliness, anger, all of the transient vividness that had brought to life her slim figure, her brown eyes, that expressive, delicately etched face, which now showed nothing but a dull certainty.

'What won't work?' he asked her, very quietly. A bird swooped by just outside the door, warbling. He watched ever on with those light, assessing eyes. For the first time, her concept of him fully meshed together; she could see his keen, analytical mind behind those eyes. Now she knew him.

'You think you're going to patch my leaky boat and get me to sail again,' she said calmly. She moved to the chair opposite him and sat down. 'You think that if you can mop me up, put me together again, and sit me down in front of a typewriter, everything is going to be peachy keen. Sunshine and roses. I'll belt out a bestseller in a frenzied four weeks, and your firm will ooze good will and the milk of human kindness all the way to the bank.'

'Actually,' he said, standing and going over to the refrigerator and opening it to peer inside at the contents. She watched him with a dull resentment. Their refrigerator, their food. He dragged out eggs and butter and milk, continuing, 'When I came, I was working and getting paid to have a meeting with you. Last night I called the office and took a leave of absence. Where are the skillets? I was on company time, yesterday. Today, I'm on my own.' Lightning electric glance at her and a slow smile, creasing his lean cheeks and making her stare. He told her, gently, 'They never would have countenanced paying me for any length of time to nurse a writer along, not even you, I'm afraid. One of my assistants would have been delegated that job.'

If she hadn't been sitting, she would have then, and hard. Her eyes, already showing evidence of the many shocks he had piled on her that day, widened even further, huge pools of darkness, pools that a person could drown in. 'You're on your own time?' she repeated in a whisper, looking over the food on the worktop, his leaning, nonchalant figure, those wide shoulders angled over lean hips, and the long, outstretched legs. 'But then—why are you doing this?'

It was a moment before he spoke, and when he

did, he spoke straight from himself, with no pretension, no wavering of his gaze, no prevarication. 'Because in these last three years, I've seen in both your letters and your stories a passionate brilliance. I've seen your writing develop from a raw talent to eloquent mastery. Because of that, because I know your past work and your potential, I can't bear to see you as you are now, lifeless, hopeless, helpless. I—guess I wouldn't be in the business at all, if I didn't care to some extent to begin with.'

Life had thrown her some cruel twists in the past few years, but she rather thought this was one of the worst. All of the conviction and hope and drive she now lacked, like a gaping rent in her personality, she saw in him as he stood before her. He really believed, deeply, truly believed, that somehow there had to be a way to rectify her present dilemma. She closed her eyes against it, her mouth a tragic bow of pain, and heard him move suddenly.

'By the way, you never did tell me where the skillets are,' he said conversationally, opening and shutting cupboards with a bang.

'What will it take to get rid of you?' she said expressionlessly, opening her eyes again to watch him move around the kitchen in concise movements. 'If I were to sit down at my typewriter right now and prove to you just how completely it's gone, would that satisfy you? Will that get you to stop tormenting me?'

He stopped and turned round, in his eyes

compassion, gentleness, regret, but his tone was brisk and businesslike. 'Of course not, don't be silly,' he replied, turning back to crack eggs into the skillet he had found. 'Today you are going to feel lousy. You are going to be an absolute wreck after you eat this meal I'm fixing you. I shouldn't be surprised if you take to your bed with a bottle of aspirin. Helen tells me you're quite a caffeine addict, and doing without coffee like you're going to will give you one mother of a headache. In fact, you're probably going to be worse than useless for the next two or three days.'

'Helen,' said she, with difficulty, 'has a lot to answer for.'

'Helen,' said Ryan firmly, 'can't handle you, and you know it. That's why she's invited me to stay here for a few weeks.'

Devan's head fell to the table at that last shocker. After a few moments, she said, the threat leaden, 'You have my personal property in the back of your car. There's nothing stopping me from calling the police and having you arrested once and for all.'

He sounded singularly unconcerned. 'I know it. But you must know me a little now that we've met and talked. I won't give up. I would be back.' He walked to the table and set a plate of fragrant, steaming eggs in front of her. 'Here, eat this. When you're no longer dependent on the caffeine, I'll bring your coffee maker back in. Then we'll see whether you are in any kind of shape for a serious writing attempt, and take it from there, all right?'

She could feel his gaze burning into the top of her bowed head, so she raised her eyes slowly. He was standing in front of her, his silence and his waiting a question. She knew he was leaving it ultimately up to her, that right at that moment she was being asked to choose which course of action she would take. But she also knew that along with her basically undisputed right of action, he had undisputedly his, and he wouldn't just give up and go away. If she gave him his chance and put up with his presence for a week or so, or however long it took, if she could prove to him once and for all that he was wrong, then he would leave and she would be left to build what fragile peace she might.

'All right,' she said, for the simple reason that she knew it wouldn't work.

CHAPTER FOUR

RYAN watched as she picked with a delicate listlessness at her hot meal. The air was awash with summer warmth and sunlit haze. From somewhere outside came the roar of Gary's Tarzan imitation, and Janie's shrieking reply. Helen was rattling around upstairs, no doubt cleaning the house. Devan could feel Ryan watching, almost in a physical touch, but she couldn't bring herself to care. He had arrived without warning and had thrown her off balance from the very beginning. She didn't have the energy to try to erect walls around herself. He could read in her what he would.

'Why the coffee maker?' she asked then, putting a forkful of egg into her mouth and chewing it. She swallowed without enthusiasm; she didn't care for runny, slimy yolks, and he'd fried her eggs a definite over-easy. 'I mean, I can see you wanting to take the liquor if I'd been a reeking alcoholic or something, but why the coffee? Half the population in America is hooked on caffeine.'

He moved, lithe and nearly silent, over to a kitchen chair and sat down, the furniture creaking under his weight. She wasn't a particularly small woman, but she felt small in comparison to him. It wasn't that he was abnormally tall, being perhaps just under six feet, but he was big and solid, with powerful, thick shoulders and muscled thighs. Even his torso, which was lean and trim in comparison to his shoulders, was full of tight solidity. 'But then other people aren't making coffee a substitute for nutritious meals like you are. You look about as starved as an alley cat,' he replied dispassionately, leaning his elbows on the table. She looked at his bare, thick forearms 'If I have my guess, your system must be on pretty shaky ground right now.'

His guess was right, and they both knew it. She looked down at her plateful of food and felt appalled. She couldn't remember getting to such a state, and was shocked to suddenly look at herself and see what she'd done. Helen's unexpected support of Ryan was more understandable to her now. While her sister hadn't nagged, she must have been watching Devan with silent worry for months now. It had taken the fresh eyes of a stranger to shake herself out of her preoccupation. Devan bent her head, a characteristic gesture of hers, and rubbed at the bridge of her nose with thumb and forefinger. The shakiness she had felt after waking and chasing Gary was getting more pronounced, and a dull throb was making itself known at the back of her left eye.

Ryan's attention had never wavered. His voice came to her quietly, 'Why don't you finish your meal while you still feel capable of it? Your head is starting to bother you, isn't it?'

She dropped her hand and in her face there was

a rejection of the sympathy in his voice as she said briefly, with a snap, 'Yeah.' She didn't want sympathy. She didn't want this man, or anyone else, reaching out to her, rejecting the half-acknowledged need in herself along with his overtures. All she wanted was for him to go away, so that she could free herself of this sneaking gratitude that was creeping up on her.

Then he stood up and went silently to the sink to start running the dishwater and set the things he had dirtied in it. She watched dully as he briskly set to work, and then her eyes swivelled to her plate, and she felt her stomach churn. She took the food and angrily shovelled it into Paris's dish, calling the cat who appeared at a dead run just a moment later. The cat settled himself neatly and then began a dainty nibbling at the unexpected meal, and Devan petted his purring back lightly. Then, with a quick glance at the back of Ryan's light brown head, she turned and made her way to the downstairs bathroom to find the aspirin bottle.

She couldn't shake off her feeling of unsteadiness and imbalance, or the stunned sense of intrusion he had invoked. Forget it, Devan, she tried to tell herself, as she took four aspirins and popped them in her mouth, swallowing them without water. As she tasted the chalky bitterness, she stared at her thin, bleak expression in the mirror. Let it run off you like rain.

But it wasn't running off her, it was seeping into her skin as though she were a greedy dry sponge, all the feelings he had brought to life again, all the

ROSE COLOURED LOVE 61

pain and insecurities, and the emptiness.

The pain behind her left eye was worsening until she began to wonder if the throbbing would push the ball right out of its socket. It was spreading to her other eye, making the light seem to pierce directly into her brain like hot needles. She thought about calling to Ryan to tell him she intended to go to bed but, with another surge of resentment, she thought, to hell with him. To hell with the world. As lousy as she was feeling, she wouldn't care if she were to disappear off the face of the planet. She stepped gingerly out of the bathroom.

And right into the path of a pelting Gary, who slammed into her torso with enough force to send them both spinning around in a circle. Devan's arms had automatically encircled his hot, wriggly body to keep him from falling, but found herself clinging to him to keep herself from losing her balance. Her mouth hung open with the surprise of his impact and her own dizzy reaction.

Gary's head raised as he found himself caught. His eyes narrowed in suspicion on Devan's white face; he hadn't a doubt that she was about to wreak vengeance on him for that afternoon, but when she leaned on him, he said, 'Hey, what's wrong with you?'

She replied through thin lips, as she tried to smile at him, 'I'm not feeling very well.'

The tow-headed urchin blinked at that. 'Oh,' he said, and then, uncharacteristically, 'I'm sorry.'

That did prompt a smile from her, and she ruffled his head as she carefully let go of him and found she could still stand on her own two feet. Then he was gone, and Devan was left to make her own way up the stairs. She was practically creeping by the time she reached her bed. She didn't bother undressing, or even dragging the covers off the floor where they'd been left since that morning; instead she fell on the sheeted mattress and buried her head under her two pillows, hoping she would never have to see the light of day again. She had time to find it simply amazing, considering her earlier nap outside, that she was quite exhausted, and then she closed her weary eyes and fell asleep.

At first it was deep and good, but then everything began to whirl on her sickeningly, and she awoke with a start, feeling sweat drying to coldness on her body, feeling the acute nausea that had brought her out of her sleep, feeling the headache which now throbbed so badly she could hardly see. Trembling, she thrust herself away from the bed, her stomach churning and twisting, and the urge to vomit grew quickly strong until she was rushing out of her room like a bullet, barely making it to the bathroom just down the hall to empty her guts, gaspingly. Dimly through her retching she heard swift, heavy footsteps sounding on the hardwood in the hall, and Ryan burst through the door she hadn't had time to latch, much less lock.

Her head came up briefly on an open-mouthed gasp, and she turned her sweat-streamed face away from him as tremors shook violently through her body. 'For God's sake, get the hell out of here!' she rasped, her arms wrapped around herself.

'Don't argue,' he said in a low voice, and he put his hand to her forehead bracingly, the other to her back. 'Damn it, I should have realised how sick this might make you, especially after tasting that strong brew last night!' There was a taut self-accusation in his voice.

It surprised her into looking at him briefly, her eyes hard brown, impenetrable bullets. Then she shook his hands off with a jerk. 'Don't worry about it,' she said thinly, through stiff lips, as nausea swept through her in a shudder. 'I can handle it.' He didn't move, just staring at her as though she were something inhuman, and then she felt the need to retch overpowering her again, and she choked out, mortified, 'Will you just get out of here?'

Her eyes had filmed over with blinding tears from the sickness, as involuntary as the saliva that filled her mouth with a rush just before she bent over the toilet again. She didn't see the sympathetic understanding that filled his light eyes, or the wincing pity as he took in her body, which was curled upon itself like a wounded creature. The spasms shook her so violently, making great sweeps through her entire frame, that she didn't have the strength to push him away a second time as his firm, strong hands came out to hold her hard against his supporting thigh. She vomited silently, as neat as a cat, the bones of her shoulders and back feeling like breakable sticks underneath her sweater. His hands tightened encouragingly on her as he felt her shake again, and her shoulders hunched in response, moving under his grip.

When the wet blindness had cleared from her eyes, the tears spilling over to run down her face and neck, when she had calmed down again, she carefully wiped her mouth, totally ignoring the man her body was so dependent on. After a moment, he reached over and flushed the toilet, and then asked her gently, 'Are you finished now, or do you still feel nauseous?'

She whispered, teeth chattering, 'I'm going to sit here for a while.' She didn't look at him when he gently set her back on the floor and then left the bathroom without a word. For a moment all she could feel was a blank uncomprehending abandonment, not in any condition to question her own emotions. He had left without an explanation, or any word at all to her. Then she understood as he returned almost immediately, holding a thick blanket from her bed which he wrapped carefully around her chilled and sweating body. She curled her trembling hands into the corners and then huddled against the wall, her face and eyes closed in on her misery.

She felt hard fingers thrusting through the hair on her forehead, pushing it back. Then they trailed down the side of her face, gently. He said in a hard, reassuring tone, 'I'll be right back. You hanging on?'

Stupid, to feel reassured, to feel a pitiful rise of responding warmth at his insistent, relentless concern, but she did. She found her lips parting, found herself whispering an acknowledgment of his help at last, 'Yeah. Thanks.'

His voice audibly softened. 'OK.' He was gone, and she let her weakness take over her body at the solitude, slipping from the wall's support like a puddle of jelly, just curling uncaringly on the bare, hard-tiled floor.

She heard low voices from the hall. Helen was asking, concernedly, 'How is she? Gary just came down to the kitchen and told me she was sick.'

'She's feeling pretty miserable,' said Ryan, quietly. 'But she'll be all right. This is the worst of it.' Devan could have sworn she heard a smile in his voice then as he said, simply, 'She's got a lot of spunk. She was mad enough when I was in there with her. She won't let me see her that wretched again, if I read things right.'

She then heard Helen's low laugh, and found herself grinning too, albeit rather weakly. Then an uncontrollable darkness swept her into its domain. Incredibly, and very quickly, she was asleep, dead to the world within one minute at the outside.

But all too soon, she felt a disturbance in that dark woolliness of her mind, and the impression of something big and dark came bending over her. She felt long, strong arms slide under her body carefully, and then she was being hoisted, slowly and gently, into Ryan's arms. She slitted her eyes. He was holding her against his chest as though she were as fragile as blown glass. He strode along the hall to her bedroom as she let her head settle in the warm hollow between his neck and shoulder, pretending, for pride's sake at her weakness, to be asleep. She could sense him looking at her thoughtfully, his bent head a dark blur through her long curling lashes, and then he was lowering her, as carefully as he'd picked her up, on to her bed.

At that she opened her eyes. He took her blanket from her after a brief and silent struggle; she had refused to give it up since she was still cold and trembling. But the exchange was more than fair, she found, as he was pulling the top sheet along with the other blankets over her, and then draping the one she'd been wrapped in over the lot, so she was content enough to slip down to her pillows.

Her face turned from him, for she expected him to leave, but he didn't. Instead, he sat down on the edge of her bed and tilted the mattress his way, so that her body rolled against his waist before she could catch herself. After a moment, he asked, 'Did you know you'd be this sick?'

She sighed, and then shrugged uninterestedly. In order to get comfortable, she turned to her side and pulled her knees up, and found that he fitted quite neatly into the hollow she'd created as she curled around him. 'It was my fault,' she said then, as his head angled to look at her. 'I took several aspirin on a near empty stomach when I wasn't feeling steady to begin with.'

Another silence, while he digested that. Then he said, musingly, 'No complaints from you, no calls for help, no admittance of weakness, not even any more rejection. Just this stoic attitude. I'd have expected anything, certainly resentment, even a little hate, but not this.' He waited. No answer. Ryan tried one more time to reach her. 'It's like,' he said, very gently, 'seeing something that's been mortally wounded and knows it, and has gone past all the anger and outrage and frustration to lie waiting for death with nothing left but a numb acceptance. Is that what you're feeling, Devan? Who or what has hurt you that badly, I wonder?'

Eyes tightly closed. No answer.

After he had eased off the bed and walked out of her room, her eyes opened and she lay for a very long time, staring at nothing.

Then she slept refreshingly, and when she next opened her eyes, darkness was beginning to creep through the open curtains of her window to settle in shadows at the corners of her bedroom. Dusk, another day gone by, a total and irrevocable waste. She stretched and lay quietly for a time, feeling her body's weakness, feeling her head pound, feeling her heart thudding far too fast. Everything felt leaden and weary; though she had slept most of the day away, it seemed that it wasn't enough, and she still felt exhausted.

She forced her quivering limbs to propel herself off the bed, and, as she still felt quite cold, she took a cardigan from the cupboard and dragged it over her sweater, buttoning it halfway up. Then she eased gingerly out of her room and down the stairs, feeling better once she was up. Helen and the children were playing a table game in the dining room, and the trio looked up interestedly at Devan's appearance.

'Gary said you up-chucked,' commented Janie dispassionately, as she juggled with a gambler's skill two dice in her hand.

Her aunt regarded her with a jaundiced eye as she marvelled, 'Tell me, Helen, were we ever so vulgar when we were their age?'

'There she goes again, calling me names I can't understand,' gloomed Janie as she threw the dice in a fit of pique, glaring at Devan. As Helen was also looking away, Devan was the only one to see Gary's hand, quick as a snake, dart out to flip one of the dice over.

'We've already eaten supper,' said Helen, 'but there's plenty left over. I'll be glad to heat you some, if you'd like.'

'Don't bother yourself, Helen,' said Ryan, from Devan's right. She turned. He had come from one of the two rooms used as a library, and he held a paperback tucked in one hand. It looked oddly small in his grip. Her eyes slid over the book incuriously and then came back to it with a sense of shock. It was her first story. She had been so infatuated with the idea of it being on the shelves in public view, she had bought a copy and then tucked it into her bookcase. As Helen had received her own copy months before, the paperback had never been read, to all intents virtually brand new.

Ryan had noted her gaze and was smiling. 'I thought I'd take a refresher course on what you've written thus far,' he said casually, with those sharp, sharp eyes. She shrugged jerkily and didn't answer. Then he asked carefully, as though expecting a

snappy retort or rebuff, 'How are you feeling? Any
steadier?'

She shrugged again, and said briefly, to the point
of terseness, 'Head hurts. That's only to be
expected.'

'Do you think you could keep something down,
if you were to eat?' he asked.

She was well aware that they had three
interested pairs of eyes watching them, and she
snapped, 'I don't know. Maybe.'

He grinned, amused, and said, 'Why don't you
relax, then, while I heat you up something?'

At that, Helen protested, 'Ryan, you don't have
to do that. I can, very easily.'

Devan watched him turn to her sister and smile.
A strange feeling invaded her at that, noting his
easy friendliness with Helen. She turned herself
and noticed, as though for the first time, how very
pretty her older sister was, looking far younger
than her thirty-two years. Ryan was saying, firmly,
'You've got enough to take care of with those two,
without having to look after Devan, too. I'll do it.'

Devan exploded. 'For God's sake! I'm not a
damned imbecilic invalid! I'm not hungry, so quit
haggling over who's going to do what for me!'
Then she turned to stalk out of the room and
hesitated. She swung back and marched over to the
table to flip the disregarded dice back. 'That was a
six, not a one.' She shook her finger under Gary's
chagrined nose. 'Cheat again, and I'll tan your
hide.'

Helen and Janie looked at him, Janie quite

indignant, and Helen warned darkly, 'And when she's finished, young man, I'll take my turn.'

He looked immediately and suitably chastened. Devan swivelled on her heel and exited to the library room which held her stereo. To discourage any company, she pushed the door shut behind her. Then, moving carefully and slowly about the room, she picked a few instrumental albums from her collection and settled them on the turntable, then switched the power on. After starting the record player, she eased herself into her deep, cushioned armchair. With the lights off, the room was in deep blue shadow, and she leaned her head back and closed her eyes.

Music pulsed in the room, low key, soothing. If she had thought she could have stood it, she would have turned the light on to read, but her head was still too tender. As Ryan had predicted, it probably would be for the next day, maybe two. She tried to get herself lost in the classical guitar music being strummed consolingly over the speakers, but she found she couldn't, found that her world had been too upset, found that, now she had the time and composure to brood, her mind was going back to things she had tried so hard to forget.

With Ryan's arrival, he had brought to the surface memories that still held for her a ragged pain, memories that showed the major flaw in her. Memories of how Lee had left her on a bright spring day, with chirping good will manifested all about her: in the sparrows which never seemed to leave New York, in the dustman who had waved at

her with a grin that morning as she had leaned out
of her brownstone apartment window to catch
sight of the morning sky. And there hadn't been
any warning; Lee had just pulled out his suitcases
and packed. When she had gone back to their
bedroom in search of him, she had found him in
the act of shutting them and pulling them off the
bed.

And she had been disbelieving, stunned, incredulous. Even as she'd asked him why, even as
she'd sat on their bed and listened to his quick,
half-angry words of reason, she hadn't believed it.
Nor had she believed it all that week, or the week
after, or that entire month. She had expected him
to come back, expected to hear his key turn in the
lock, expected him to call, or write, or contact her
in some way. Hurting, but expecting, and willing
to believe again, to have faith and goodness shine
upon her again, to have sanity reign in the
barrenness of his passing, but none of it had come.

Then, finally, she had had to accept the truth of
what he had told her.

Sudden light flooded the room, making her start
and blink, making hasty hands rise to her face to
wipe uselessly at the tears which had made paths of
wetness down her throat. Her eyes flew to the door
in disconcertment, but if she had thought she was
startled, it was nothing to the naked expression of
shock she saw on Ryan's face as he stared at her,
utterly immobile. His light, blue-grey eyes raked
over her, and then he strode to her side and knelt
by her chair, the movement a rush. Her blurred

eyes noted fleetingly that Helen and the children had left the dining room. She had the frightening sensation of being overwhelmed, and then his hands were gripping at her forearms.

'Why are you crying?' he asked, the query throbbing.

'Don't pry at me,' she gritted, trying to draw back, but she was too trembly and he was able to hold her with an almost contemptuous effortlessness.

'This last day I've seen you in varying moods of hostility, resentment and anger. I've even seen despair, but you never cried,' he said, low and intense, his hard face too close. 'Not even when you told me you had no hope, no faith. Why are you crying now? What is it? Discouragement? Are you sick? Dammit, this is important, can't you see that? If you would let it out, maybe you could *heal* and become the Devan you used to be, the one I've known and admired! Is it fear, are you afraid?'

'Stop prying at me!' she cried hoarsely, her throat raw and working. And then something else he had never seen from her showed briefly in her eyes, showing wild, and it was blind panic.

He backed away immediately, his hands falling to his sides as he stood and went to the open doorway. He hesitated with his back to her, the muscles in his neck and shoulders visibly taut. He then said, with difficulty, 'I'm very sorry. I pushed too hard. It was wrong of me. You're too weak.'

His head went down and then he walked away as though he were very tired. She stared at the open doorway and, curiously enough, when she came to herself with a start, all the clamouring voices from the past were peacefully silent.

After a time, she rose and walked carefully out of the room. The kitchen light was on, so she went to the back of the house and found Ryan serving a simple, yet well-cooked supper on to a plate. He was unaware of her presence in that open doorway, and she stood and contemplated him thoughtfully. There was impatience and anger in his movements as he worked, and while she couldn't guess at what had prompted the emotions in him, she could see how characteristically he expressed them. This man would be patient, she felt, with few things.

Her head was aching worse than ever, so she went to the bathroom and took only two aspirins this time. When she then made her way back to the kitchen, she pretended to no secrecy and sat quietly at the table while she watched him finish.

All appearance of impatience and anger were wiped away as if they'd never been. He turned and smiled at her, warily, yet friendly enough. She noted the wariness with some dryness; she'd certainly given him cause to tread rather carefully around her. She had the sudden suspicion that he was treating her with velvet gloves, and she began to wonder why.

'French toast sandwiches tonight,' he said conversationally, turning back to the worktop again. 'I got fresh bread at the bakery earlier, when you were asleep. They're good.'

'They sound good,' she said, her tone bringing

his head quickly around again. She had spoken mildly, even with friendliness.

He then asked, slowly, 'Will you at least *try* to eat some of this?'

One corner of her lips rose, ever so slightly. 'Yes,' she said.

His expression lightened, almost imperceptibly. 'Good,' he replied.

He sat with her while she ate. The meal was silent, though not necessarily in a negative way. She knew his eyes were on her with approval as she managed to eat fully half of her sandwich, along with her entire portion of vegetables, and part of a fresh peach. She was sipping at a glass of milk when he finally said, 'You haven't done badly at all. How are you feeling—do you think you can keep it down?'

'I think so,' she said lightly, and then she downed the rest of her milk. 'I feel much steadier. This must be the most I've eaten in two days.'

She thought he winced. 'No wonder you're thin,' he said, caustically. He then surveyed her plate. 'Are you going to be able to manage the rest of that?'

She looked down, doubtfully. 'N-no. I think I'm wary of pushing it.'

'Wise child. It'd be best if you can keep down what you've eaten, rather than risk losing the whole meal. Well, then, hand it over,' he told her.

'What?' she asked, both looking and sounding startled.

His brows rose slightly, his eyes smiling. 'You

surely don't expect to throw all that good food away, do you?' he returned, reaching over with his long arm and plucking the plate from under her gaze. 'It might be a sadly over-used cliché, but there do happen to be starving people in the world, and I abhor wanton waste.'

She smiled. It was the first real, open, genuine, un-bitter smile she'd given him, and his eyes widened on her face for a moment before a pleasant mask came over his features and he bent his head to finish her meal. 'I suppose there was logic in that statement,' she remarked, doubtfully, and a positively surreptitious look of delight crept over his face as he realised she was actually teasing him.

She sat with him while he finished, and then stood to help stack the pots and her set of crockery. He wouldn't let her help wash up, though she tried to insist, and finally he took her by the elbows and steered her over to a chair. Then he went to the kitchen drawers to pull out a tea towel. He threw it into her lap with a neat flick of his wrist.

'There,' he said, implacably. 'Now don't *argue* with me on this one, all right? Hell's bells, you're an impossible creature! You may be feeling steadier than you were, but that's not such a big improvement, when you consider this afternoon! Tomorrow, or the day after, you can cook for everybody *and* wash up, if it'll make you feel better.'

'Not necessarily,' she replied drily. 'If you want to do it so badly, why, go right ahead!'

She wasn't sure how she had meant that, but she found herself pleased when he laughed in response. He ran the dishwater, plunged his arms into masses of white suds, and proceeded very quickly to wash everything that had been dirtied, rinsing and then handing the things to her almost faster than she could dry them. When they were done, everything put away and the worktop again neatly bare, he turned to dry his hands and look at her with a smile. That steady, blue-grey gaze brought her to the sudden realisation that they had just spent a very enjoyable, tension-free hour together. She grew so flustered, she actually, obviously blushed, and his smile widened. But all he said was, 'Now that that's done, let's go and watch television.' She sat immobile, full of an odd emotion, but he didn't give her time to start an argument. He just plucked her from the seat as firmly as he had deposited her, and steered her to the front of the house. 'I wonder if there's a good movie on.'

CHAPTER FIVE

DEVAN couldn't have been more aware of the heavy hand he laid on her shoulder if it had burned a hole through her clothes. Because of it, she contented herself with shrugging uninterestedly at his idle comment, and in this way they passed to the living room. Helen and the children were watching a comedy. The lights were off, so silver reflections sparkled in their eyes. Helen was seated in a large, sagging armchair and Janie was just in front of her, between her legs, while her mother brushed her carrot-coloured, gleaming hair. Gary was sprawled on the couch and kicking at one arm.

Devan scooped up her nephew so that she and Ryan had a place to sit without resorting to the floor, and she was much surprised to find that, as she settled on to the cushions, Gary seemed disposed to settle right along with her. Typically, he ignored her even as he wriggled his thin body close, so, with a dry smile, she put her arm around him and then calmly turned her attention to the screen. The couch sagged as Ryan sat down then, too, and for half an hour quiet reigned peacefully over the group.

Even as Devan marvelled at the enjoyable silence, it disappeared. As the credits for the show flashed on the screen, Helen stirred herself and said firmly, 'OK, that's it, kids. Time for bed.'

A chorus of protest resounded then. In the end, Devan had to get out of her seat and half drag, half carry a limp Gary up the stairs for her sister, while Janie volubly complained every step of the way. Thankfully, Devan deposited her load with a none too gentle thump on the floor of the bathroom, and then she backed out to make her escape back down the stairs.

She fell into her seat again with such eloquence that Ryan laughed and shook his head. She turned to look at him with a twisted grin, and then she asked, 'Do you remember ever acting like that when you were a kid?'

A hard white smile creased his face as he thought of that. 'No, I can't say I do,' he said. He had one arm draped over the back of the couch, and one leg hooked nonchalantly up on the cushions. In casual jeans and a light green shirt, he appeared quite relaxed. 'As I recall, the adults were the unreasonable ones, not I.'

'Did you have any brothers or sisters to play with?' Devan reached to a nearby table for the TV guide Helen always bought and began to flip through the listings. There weren't any movies on, but a rather interesting musical special was, so she rose to change the channels while he replied,

'I had two younger brothers. We always found something to get into, it seems. Then somewhere along the line, something changed. They're settled in New Jersey, close to my parents, while I got a sort of urban wanderlust. I moved to Boston and then to Philadelphia, before coming to New York, and as for my family, we—keep in touch.'

'Birthday and Christmas cards,' she commented. Helen appeared in the archway, made for her chair, and sank into it with a gesture startlingly reminiscent of Devan's.

'That's about the extent of it,' he admitted, and then sent a smiling glance over to Helen. 'I'm certainly nowhere as close to my family as you two seem to be.'

Devan's face closed over as she thought of their childhood, but Helen merely lightly replied, 'We're only able to manage that because we're as different as night and day.' A long series of commercials was drawing to an end, and the opening of the music special reeled by. Then Devan's sister spoke, absently, 'Oh, yes, Ryan, I've put sheets on your bed. It's the first door on your left at the top of the stairs.'

'You didn't need to go to the trouble. I could have done it.'

Devan was silent, wrapped in her thoughts.

'Nonsense,' said Helen, firmly. Then, 'What's this?'

'A Sara Bertelli special,' said Devan, absently. Reflected colours showed in the brown of her eyes and, in the darkened room the thinness of her facial features and body structure was hidden, making her appear much softer. She felt very strange for a moment; the three of them seemed so ordinary and prosaic, as though watching television together and chatting happened all the time.

'I'm a great fan of hers,' said Ryan as he stretched, long legs going out, his ribcage expanding. Then he settled again, his hands laced at the back of his head.

Devan tried to shake off her mood, and said rather wryly, 'Most people are.'

'I take it you're not?'

'Oh, no, I didn't mean that,' she replied mildly. 'I happen to like her quite a bit, myself. What I meant was that it's rather hard not to—she seems to have a very endearing personality.' Then she frowned at the screen as the singer came on the studio stage, blazing with vivacity, electricity, dashing style. She was singing a song Devan had never heard before. 'Wait—this doesn't look at all like the one I've seen. It must be a new special.'

Ryan picked up the TV guide and looked at it carelessly. 'This says it's her second. Was her first any good?'

'Excellent,' she said, and their idle chatting was suspended for a time as all three concentrated on the network special. During the commercials they talked lightly, but not much. Devan found, to her surprise, that she had quite relaxed, and was feeling almost good again, except for the persistent, nagging ache behind her left eye.

Ryan kicked off his shoes and crossed his ankles, slouching very comfortably as though he had nothing better to do with his time than laze a summer evening away. His hair was casually ruffled, and his light eyes seemed to stand out against his darker face whenever she glanced at him. His shirt sleeves were still rolled up from having washed the dishes, and the top three buttons of his shirt were carelessly undone, as though he couldn't bear the confines of his collar. With his legs stretched out halfway across the living room floor, the material of his slacks was pulled tight across hips and thigh muscles.

She watched as he frowned slightly towards the end of the programme. Then he said musingly, 'I read something about her, a while ago. Now, what was it?'

Devan replied absently, curling her legs underneath her neatly, 'She was nearly another John Lennon, if that's what you mean. Some crazy shot her down in the street.'

His eyes followed the slim, bright figure now saying her goodbye, looking so real, yet thousands of miles away, and unaware of their existence. 'That's right, and her husband was the prosecuting attorney for the case; I remember now. The guy pleaded temporary insanity.'

Her attention was caught now by him, no longer held by the televison, and she waited for him to continue. When he didn't, she prompted, 'Yeah, so what happened?'

He looked mildly startled. 'I thought you already knew.'

'I didn't follow the story. I'd been—busy at the time.' She had been grieving at the time, waiting for Lee to contact her, isolated in her suspended existence, shut in on herself.

Helen spoke up unexpectedly from her armchair. 'As I remember, the fellow who had shot her had tried something of the kind before and got off on a technicality. The jury didn't buy his plea, and he was put away on maximum sentence, attempted murder.' She shuddered then, delicately.

Devan glanced at her sister and then she shrugged. 'One more nut off the street, I guess.'

Ryan grunted, watching the last scenes of the singer with fascination. Then he said, 'Look at her, doesn't she look marvellous? This must have been filmed after her recovery—she doesn't show a bit of it, does she? Vital, and dynamic—even her singing volume seems to be unimpaired. Can you imagine,' he said, musingly, 'what she must have gone through in this last year? Pain, shock, fear, near death. And to see her now, she's going strong.'

His words were very casual, almost too casual, and Devan turned her head sharply to stare at him. Then her whole expression changed, for she knew what he was saying underneath the light conversation, what he was trying to convey to her in a roundabout way. She stood abruptly, walked over to the television to turn it off, cutting the singer off in mid-chorus.

'Devan!' protested Helen.

But she didn't listen as she pivoted to make for the stairs. 'Good try,' she drawled.

His voice softly reached her. 'It was a good try, but the question is, did it work?'

Her steps faltered, then totally stopped. Images of the singer's radiant, sleek happiness were played

back through her mind, and a sudden, intense
wave of anger pulsed through her. 'No,' she said
bitterly, all her former hostility for him surging
back and doing fine.

'But why not?' he asked quietly, and the couch
springs creaked. Then she heard him walking her
way. 'It seems to me that she's a great example of
fortitude and hope.'

She exploded, 'The situation is *not* the same;
how can you say that?' Then she whirled, to
confront him with her anger. 'Are you that blind?
Her conflict was external, not internal, like mine!
She had a whole different set of problems to
overcome!' And a supportive, loyal husband who
helped her overcome them. 'Besides——'

He was watching her keenly, alertly, in the
indirect wash of light from the hall, his entire
expression vivid and unsurprised by her outburst.
She stared at him, and then knew that he had been
pushing her again. And he was pushing her now as
he said quietly, 'Besides—what, Devan?'

She spoke the bitter words deliberately, 'What I
wrote was a lie,' and she knew she'd got him. As
shock came like a douse of icy water over his
features, she turned and left the room.

My God, she thought, a few moments later, as
she fell into her bed. When will I ever get enough
sleep? She was immensely thankful when uncon-
sciousness crept over her to make her unaware of
the dull heaviness sitting in her chest.

Downstairs, Ryan turned as if careful of his
balance and he stared at Devan's older sister for a

moment before asking, softly, 'What in God's name did she mean by that?'

Helen said, hushed, 'I don't know. She never would talk to me about it.'

The next morning, Devan awoke very early, and she lay for a few minutes listening to the birds singing outside her window. It then occurred to her that this was the earliest she had awakened in a long time, and she rolled over to try to go back to sleep, but found she couldn't after so much yesterday. Then she threw off her covers and stood to stretch cautiously. The persistent nagging pain behind her left eye was still present, but much diminished, and she found that she could ignore it well enough if she tried. By tomorrow, it would be totally gone.

She showered and washed her hair, taking care to be very quiet as nobody else was awake, and then, after dressing, she descended the stairs. With the lights off and the rooms unoccupied, the living room and dining room seemed cold and bleak. She hesitated on the bottom step for no good reason, feeling forlorn. The thought of Ryan flooded through her and she grimaced wryly. In the last two days she had been as terse and as unwelcoming as possible. Remorse and regret filled her, but she pushed it down. He had forced himself into her life. He wasn't wanted. Perhaps now he would leave.

She stepped off the bottom stair and passed through the dining room, looking idly into one of the rooms that shot off to the right of it, for the light was on and that was unusually careless of Helen, who always made a tour of the downstairs before she went to bed. When she looked briefly in, she stopped dead.

Ryan was sitting in the armchair, his head bowed, his face lined with a great tiredness, the firm mouth set. His light brown hair was wildly awry, his light grey-blue eyes staring at the floor in front of him, unfocused. His broad shoulders were slumped, his arms lying along the rests, the hands together in his lap and laced loosely. To the side of the chair was a half empty cup of what looked like coffee, and several stacked books.

Her books.

And then she realised he was wearing the clothes he had worn the day before. She took all that in in a split second, and then he was glancing up at her expressionlessly. That quiet look was devoid of everything, and it sent an inexplicable chill down her spine, for she'd never seen him look that way before. She gestured with her hand. 'That looks like coffee,' she said.

He didn't look over the side of his chair. 'It is,' was his brief reply. Then he raised one hand and rubbed at his chin, feeling whiskers. 'There's more in the kitchen, if you want it.'

She stood quite still, feeling her understanding of the situation slip away from her. It wasn't a nice feeling at all; at least, before, she thought she knew what to expect of him, and what he expected of her. Now she didn't know anything. Her eyes moved over him, arrested. 'What are you playing at?' she asked, slowly. He didn't reply, so she pressed, 'You've been up all night, haven't you?'

His head went back to rest on the chair. 'Yes.'

Devan let her eyes roam over the room putting the pieces together, assessing, judging. Then she felt hurt and was angry at herself for it. It was wrong to feel hurt, wrong because she should have expected it, should have realised this would happen, should have known. But the pain was there, in her eyes before she could hide it, bleeding. He, too, had given up on her. His head came up and he was staring at her, his light eyes narrowed, his expression unreadable. 'It's over, then?' she asked flippantly and, without waiting to hear the words, she headed towards the kitchen and the waiting coffee.

She should have remembered how fast he could move, but she hadn't, and was jolted to the core when he came up behind her, put his violent hands on her shoulders and practically threw her around and into the wall. She made a sound of fright deep in her throat, and would have moved if she'd had the chance, but he was already on her, his hands slammed on either side of her head, his body holding her in place by weight.

She was looking up with huge eyes into his, and was shocked even further at the rage and sneaking pain that was hard in his face. He brought his head down to hers, and he whispered through his teeth, 'No, it's not over.' She felt a wild trembling course through her, and shut her eyes against that look of him. Then she felt his hands in her hair, roughly thrust, jerking her head. 'Look at me!' Really frightened then, she did, her body shrinking from his and the feel of those hard, pressing muscles.

She said on a half moan, 'What's wrong with you?'

He shook her, making her cry out, and he shouted in a deep voice, 'What the hell is wrong with *you*?'

'Stop it!' Her hands were futilely on his wrists.

'Stop it! Go away! Leave me be!' he roared, and his face was lost to her in the rush of damnable, blinding, unexpected tears that filled her eyes, spilling out. Then he growled, 'Do you know what I did last night? You shook me, you really did, by what you'd said. I couldn't believe it. I couldn't accept that something and someone I've had confidence in for three years could be such a lie. You shook my faith in myself, and my own perceptions, and so I read your books again. It was all there, the conviction, that fine passion, truth, God, your beautiful poetry! Your characters have some of the most sensitive and compelling relationships I've ever read—how can you call that a lie? How can you believe that of yourself? Do you, really? If you do, you're not at all the person I thought you were!'

Helen had sent her wakened children back to their rooms as it was before six, and she'd come down the stairs herself, worried at the sudden uproar. She stood quietly for a few moments, looking on the two who were quite unaware of her, and then she turned and silently went back to her own room, her face quite thoughtful.

Devan's face was breaking into anguish, her hands digging like talons into the corded strength of his wrists. 'It has to be a lie,' she whispered, her breath coming harsh and uneven. 'It has to be.'

His forehead was down on hers, his shoulders bunched as his hands forced her to remain in that close, revealing position. She was off balance, not knowing or understanding how she managed to stand, everything awhirl inside of her. She felt as though he had taken his two hands and ripped the fabric of herself wide open and was looking deep into her at the hurt which had scarred but never really healed, which bled sluggishly at the wincing touch of air.

'Why?' He spoke the word with stiffened lips.

She cried, and it was a thin, faint scream of pain, 'Because nothing else makes any sense!'

'*Why?*'

But then she was really sobbing, with body racking, ear hurting, low, raw, harsh-sounding sobs, and her body was shaking so that she would indeed have fallen had he not held her so tightly, so roughly. All she could manage to say was a low litany of, 'Leave me alone, g-go away, for God's sake, can't you see how you're hurting me? Can't you see? I hurt!'

Through her haze of shaking wet blindness, she could feel him breathing hard and deep as if he had run a long race, his body as tight and tense as steel. She couldn't see to know that his eyes were watching her face with a deep horror and wincing compassion. Then he said, as if he couldn't stand it, the words coming to her faintly, 'Stop it. Ssh, don't. Stop.'

But she couldn't, for she was a helpless victim of the weeping that had taken hold of her body, the tears running into her mouth. She tasted salt, and then, with a groan, he put his open mouth over hers. Through the salt of her tears, she tasted coffee on his wet, warm breath, and she felt the slight stubble of his beard rasp at her lips, reddening them. She had time to discern that it wasn't a kiss at all, but a mouth to mouth pressure, an aggression of himself imposed on herself, a force he was making her realise. He pressed those rough, rasping, hurting lips all over her wet face as he cradled her head. 'Stop it,' he said in a low voice. 'Stop it.'

It worked; the sobs stilled. She breathed hard, uttering something that was appallingly like a whimper, and her hands slipped from his wrists. His own hands were loosening, and she felt herself slide along the wall as if she would fall, and her hands went involuntarily to grip the front of his shirt. He trembled, once, and then pulled her into his arms, wrapping them tight around her body, holding her hard against him. With one hand, he pressed her head into the hollow of his neck and shoulder, his legs braced wide apart to support both their weights.

She heard herself say, dully, 'You're giving up on me. You're giving up.'

He shook his head sharply, his jaw knocking her temple. 'No, I'm not.'

'Then you're a fool.' She held on to him tightly. 'I don't have anything in me, I don't have anything.'

His hand crushed her against the hardness of his collar bone. 'Shut up.'

But she persisted, 'You were, you know it. You were going to quit.' Her mouth moved on him as she said the words, he was holding her so tightly. She couldn't get in a deep breath.

But then he was loosening his arms, holding her away by her shoulders so that he could see her face. Those light eyes weren't light at all, she found, as she stared back. They were a deep, stormy blue with large pools of blackness. He said, 'I was. Before. If what you'd said was true, I could be now. But it isn't. You do have something. You have so much pain inside you, you're a reeking well of hurting. It makes me hurt just to be near you, you're so full of it.'

She looked away. 'Then don't get near me.'

He continued, as if she hadn't spoken, 'I might have known you would be like this. Everything you feel is so intense, it dominates your entire being, doesn't it? All that marvellous passion isn't gone from you, it's crippled by something I don't know. Something about you, something that's happened to you, something that's hurt you so badly, you don't know how to get yourself out of it. Something I've got to find out.'

Relentless words. She shook her head against his blind determination. He still couldn't see. 'Ryan, it won't work. Take my word for it.'

He smiled then, faintly, passing his hand gently over her still damp hair. 'I almost did. You project your feelings so intensely, I was beginning to get swamped by that stubborn conviction of yours. You nearly got to me last night, until I took that step back to look at you for what you really are. You won't shake me again.'

She had a sudden fear that he would shake her, though, as he had from the very beginning, as he had over and over again. She felt an apprehensive dread of the near future. What would happen? What would he stir in her? What would he do when he finally did realise that his efforts were futile? How could you build something out of dead ashes?

He let her go, his hands hovering for a moment as he waited to see if she could support herself, which she did, her knees locking into stiffness, one of her hands going behind her to splay out against the wall. She watched him turn and walk away, and he threw absently over his shoulder, 'Oh yes, and the coffee's off limits for you again, until the end of the week.'

'I could just go into town and buy a new machine!' she snapped, feeling the display of ill temper steady her.

It made him throw back his head and laugh as he disappeared into the kitchen, a merry, truly amused sound. 'You do that,' he shouted, the words wafting back to her, 'and I'll take that away, too!'

She sighed gustily, rubbing at her itchy eyes.

Crying always made her feel worse than terrible, and her head was throbbing full out. She contemplated going to the kitchen to pour herself a cup of coffee despite his admonition, but he was probably halfway to his car with the machine by now. She went to the bathroom instead, and took a dose of aspirin. Besides, she found she had a sneaky determination to cut back on her caffeine intake, anyway. Of course it had nothing to do with Ryan. That was pure coincidence.

A moment later, he was shouting at her again. 'Will you come on, for Pete's sake? What's taking you so long?'

She had been splashing cold water on her face, and her head came up with a snap at that. Then she was yelling, furiously, her head pounding with the pressure of it, 'Don't you be thinking you can give me any damned orders, mister!'

He was in the open doorway of the bathroom then, and regarding her with overtly astonished eyes. But she could see the wicked enjoyment behind it all, and suddenly she felt good. Not great, not profound, but simply, quietly good. 'But I wasn't ordering you,' he said limpidly. 'I thought you were coming to the kitchen, so I started your breakfast. Come on, it's getting cold.'

She grumbled, allowing him to drag her along behind him, 'I'm not hungry.'

He retorted, 'You're never hungry. If I held my breath for that, you'd pine away. Now, sit. Eat.'

She took one look at the fragrant steaming eggs, ham and toast laid attractively on a plate and turned away, shuddering visibly. 'There's no way,' she said simply, with difficulty. 'I am absolutely, positively not going to eat that. No doubt about it.'

This time he really was astonished, looking from the plate to her again. 'But why not?'

'In the not so distant past,' she gritted, smelling the egg and beginning to feel sick, 'I happen to have vomited after eating over-easy eggs. I'm sorry. Thank you for cooking it, but I cannot.'

'Oh,' he said blankly, and then, 'Well, I can make the eggs disappear, but what about the rest? You haven't a learned aversion to ham and toast, have you?'

She peeked again, uncertainly. 'Er, I don't think so.'

He took the plate, whisked the offending eggs off to another, and then slapped the first with the rest of the food on to the table. 'There you go,' he told her cheerfully. Then for good measure, he went to the refrigerator and pulled out a fresh orange. 'Do you like fruit?'

'Yes,' she said weakly, feeling bulldozed.

He pulled back her chair with his one free hand. She sank into it slowly. Then, as she began on the salty, juicy ham and crunchy buttered toast, he sat and peeled the orange. She started to follow his movements with her eyes, watching as he fragmented the segments. By the time he was finished, she fell on it ravenously, the fresh sweetness tasting better than anything had for a long time. He leaned back in his chair with a smile. When she glanced at him and stopped, an orange segment halfway to her mouth, a stricken look coming over her features, he visibly tensed.

She looked at the fruit she held, and set it carefully back down. 'You look tired,' she said quietly.

'Perhaps,' he said, with some dryness, watching her closely, 'because I am tired.' Her expression went smoothly blank. His eyes sharpened. Then he went on, casually, 'Are you going to blame yourself for that? You shouldn't. It was entirely my own doing, I assure you.'

'Yes,' she agreed tonelessly, pushing the segment around with her forefinger, delicately. 'You did it because you cared. You're here because you care.' Something came and went in her expression, fleeting but so vivid and intense he unconsciously sat forward and held his breath. She stood and walked slowly away, stopping at the open entrance of the dining room. She said painfully, her back to him, 'Don't care about me, Ryan. I don't have anything to give in return.'

She walked out, and the kitchen seemed to echo briefly with her words, and then with emptiness. 'That's not true,' he whispered, though she wasn't there to hear. He bent his head and shaded his eyes with his hand.

CHAPTER SIX

DEVAN met Helen, Gary and Janie at the bottom of the staircase as the three finally came down for breakfast. She mumbled something under the heat of her sister's interested gaze, and then hurried up to her room. After about fifteen minutes or so of feverish activity, during which she made her bed, straightened her wardrobe, and totally rearranged two dressing-table drawers, she stopped, resting her head against the open third drawer, her hands tightening on its handles. She felt she was suffocating under Ryan's continuous presence, and under the weight of her own chaotic thought. Then she slammed shut the drawer, whisked up her shoes and purse, and clattered back down the stairs.

In the kitchen, Janie was finishing her breakfast while Gary, an inherent gobbler and already done, was sneaking bits of food to a furtive Paris; Helen nibbled at a piece of toast and pretended that she didn't see. Ryan was nowhere in sight.

They all looked up at her entrance. 'I'm going to town for a little while,' she said shortly as she plopped in a chair and tugged on her shoes. Her sister raised calm eyebrows but didn't comment. Devan didn't know why she felt goaded into explaining, 'I need some space. It'll do me good to get out of the house.'

Helen swallowed around a piece of crust and said mildly, 'Nobody was arguing with you.'

Devan's head snapped up from tying her shoelaces, and she looked from gaze to gaze. 'Well,' she said, too brightly. 'I guess I'll see you guys later.'

'Can I come?' asked Janie, with her mouth full of cornflakes. She was dressed in faded overalls, and her carrot hair was braided at the back.

'Me, too,' said Gary, immediately.

'No,' said Devan, repellingly.

Neither took heed, as they both began to clamour a cacophonous complaint. Devan tried to stem the flow but was unsuccessful, and when she looked to Helen pleadingly, her sister just sat back and smiled, not about to get involved in the subject.

'No, and that's all there is to it!' Devan exclaimed, putting her foot down, and bringing to an abrupt halt the children's expostulations. 'I am going by myself. I want some peace and, above all, I want some quiet. There's no way I'd get either if you two monsters came along. I'll take you to town some other time. Not today. Definitely not.'

Janie hung her head, abjectly. 'I can be quiet. I've got some money I could have shopped with,' she said forlornly. 'Even Gary got to go when he went to the dentist. I never get to go anywhere.'

Gary followed his older sister's lead. 'And I have a dollar,' he said pathetically.

Discover a world of romance and intrigue in days gone by with 2 Masquerade historical romances FREE.

Every Masquerade historical romance brings the past alive with characters more real and fascinating than you'll find in any history book.

Now these wonderful love stories are combined with more real historical detail than ever before with 256 pages of splendour, excitement and romance. You'll find the heroes and heroines of these spellbinding stories are unmistakeably real men and women with desires and yearnings you will recognise. Find out why thousands of historical romance lovers rely on Masquerade to bring them the very best novels by the leading authors of historical romance.

And, as a special introduction we will send you 2 exciting Masquerade romances together with a dazzling diamond zirconia necklace FREE when you complete and return this card.

As a regular reader of Masquerade historical romances you could enjoy a whole range of special benefits — a free monthly newsletter packed with recipes, competitions, exclusive book offers and a monthly guide to the stars, plus extra bargain offers and big cash savings.

When you return this card we will reserve a Reader Service subscription for you. Every 2 months you will receive four brand new Masquerade romances, delivered to your door postage and packing free. There is no obligation or commitment — you can cancel or suspend your subscription at any time.

It's so easy, send no money now — you don't even need a stamp. Just fill in and detach this card and send it off today.

TWO FREE BOOKS as your introduction to MASQUERADE

Hazel Smith
Gypsy Royal

LOVE and WAR
Mary Nichols

MASQUERADE

Plus this beautiful diamond zirconia NECKLACE – FREE

FREE BOOKS CERTIFICATE

Dear Susan,

Your special introductory offer of 2 free books is too good to miss. I understand that are mine, to keep with the free necklace. Please also reserve a Reader Service subscription for me. If I decide to subscribe, I shall receive four brand new Masquerade romances every other month, for just £6.00, post and packing free. If I decide not to subscribe, I shall write to you within 10 days. The free books are mine to keep in any case.

I understand that I may cancel or suspend my subscription at any time by writing to you. I am over 18 years of age.

2A7M

Name _____
(BLOCK CAPITALS PLEASE)
Address _____

Signature _____

_____ Postcode _____

To Susan Welland
Reader Service
FREEPOST
P.O. Box 236
CROYDON
Surrey CR9 9EL

SEND NO MONEY NOW

Devan's eyes grew harassed. 'You think you're going to sucker me with emotional blackmail,' she accused. 'Well, it's not going to work. Now, for the last time, I said no!'

Ten minutes later, Devan was carefully backing around Ryan's parked rented car. She didn't breathe until she was pulling around its gleaming back bumper. Then she said, irritably, 'Gary, if you don't stop fiddling with that seatbelt and snap it on, I'm going to throw you both out of the car.' She stopped at the end of the driveway until she heard from the back seat a definite snick as the buckle was fastened in place. She nodded, placidly. 'That's better.' Then she pulled out, and started sedately down the road.

While she drove, Devan brooded from under her levelly held brows at the sunny day. The children's comfortable bickering floated over the back seat and washed over her and out of the window. She didn't pay any attention. Her mind was dwelling on that morning's painful clash with Ryan. She just couldn't stand being in the house with him; she needed to think, away from the tensions that had dogged her footsteps ever since he had arrived. Already they had had more confrontations than she cared to remember. She was now feeling an overriding desire to experience simple, everyday life, and normal smiles. She wanted to have uncomplicated, shallow interactions with the bookshop assistant, the waitress at the delicatessen, the cashier at the chemist.

She parked in the street, and then turned to

present her most fierce expression to the pair in the back seat of her sister's car. They looked suitably impressed. Gary even grimaced back. 'Now,' said Devan, pleasantly. 'You two are going to behave yourselves. You are going to be polite, and say please and thank you to anyone you purchase from. You are going to stick by me. You are not going to run through the stores, and you will not make any bird calls, loud whistles, or otherwise undue noise while we are in public. Got that?'

They nodded solemnly. Devan smiled. 'OK, let's go.'

She took them to the bookshop first, figuring that they would behave better at the start than later on, and she was right. Both Janie and Gary browsed quietly while Devan looked over the new publications shelf. She felt a warm surge of affection for the two as she looked over the shelf to observe them reading in the funny card section. Janie was helping Gary with the words that were too big for him, and their heads, bent together, gleamed gold and red. Devan gathered the books she wanted to buy under her arm and made for the cashier. When the children joined her, she looked down. Janie had picked up a book, an enamelled brooch, and a chocolate bar, while Gary was clutching both a chocolate bar and a Snoopy pencil. It brought an involuntary smile to her face.

'How much money did you say you had?' she asked Gary. He dug out of his pocket a handful of change and presented it as evidence. They counted it over together while they waited in line, and

Devan raised her brows. 'You do realise that you don't have enough for the sales tax?'

He looked crestfallen. Janie said, defensive of her arithmetic as she had helped him pick his purchases, 'He must have a hole in his pocket, 'cause he had a dollar twenty when we left the house.'

Devan sent a quick glance down Gary's patched and battered blue jeans and could well believe it. 'How much do you have?' she asked her niece.

'Five dollars.'

'I see.' The customer ahead of them was just paying, so she hurried to say, 'Look, we're going to look around some more. If you'll put away the chocolate, I'll buy you two some ice-cream a little later. Then you can look around a bit before you decide on what you want to buy. If you still want these things, we'll come back for them, all right?'

'Yeah!' They scrambled to put their purchases back where they'd found them while Devan paid for her books. Then she made Gary hand over his money so that he wouldn't lose any more, and they trooped over to the drugstore.

Devan brooded over an expensive shampoo and hair conditioner, and Janie found an enamelled brooch that was much cheaper. But of the three, Gary was the one to lose his heart totally, to a Luke Skywalker Jedi black plastic kite over which he mooned despairingly, for it cost three ninety-five. Devan watched as his stubby little hands touched at the plastic wrapping one more time before sliding it back on the rack, and she couldn't take it.

And so it was that, five minutes later, the three of them were walking out of the store and Gary was the most ecstatic, his fine blond hair positively vibrating with delight.

He skipped to catch up with his aunt. 'Can I put it together now?'

'No, Gary. It'll be to big to carry around. Just wait until we get home and I'll help you assemble it.'

'Oh, please! I'll sit in the car with it while you two go to other stores,' he offered magnanimously.

'No, Gary! You'd get the string tangled up, and the plastic might get holes in it. You'd better wait until we get home. There's nowhere to fly it here, anyway.' Devan lifted her head to the fresh breeze which was playing with her hair. She waited for him to argue, but he subsided rather amazingly, so she smiled, pleased.

After they had toured the only department store in town, Janie went back to buy her book. They went next to the delicatessen, which also sold ice-cream cones and, after buying for the children, Devan ordered herself a lemonade. Then the three went to a booth to enjoy their treat. Janie had put on her brooch and was continuously twisting to see what it looked like, and Gary busied himself with pushing his ice-cream scoops into the hollowed cone, with the result that his face became smeared with chocolate. Devan was sitting beside Janie on the outside of the booth, and she swung her legs idly against the black and white tiled floor. As she sipped at her tart, cold drink, she stared at the scarred tiling rather distantly. The rumble of an approaching vehicle sent her preoccupied gaze to the window, and she watched as their postman whizzed by in his ancient, battered truck. She pushed her glossy black hair from her face, and felt the heat of her sun-warmed skin.

A shiver ran through her body convulsively. Her raw sobbing from earlier, and Ryan's urgent, physical response. Her hand went to her cheek in wonder, remembering how he had shocked her, and how the shock had been like a steadying slap in the face. The remembrance made her feel acutely uncomfortable, for at the time it had not been a sexual overture, but now, in retrospect, she could recall his hands gripping her, his hard mouth and body, the way he had surrounded and overwhelmed her. She shivered again, and felt an unexpected wave of fierce hunger in her body. She was hungry, hungry to know and experience her own sexuality again, hungry for the give and take of lovemaking, hungry for caresses and murmurings low in her ear, hungry for body rhythms and sweating passion.

Hungry.

Somebody asked her something, and she shook free of her acutely uncomfortable train of thought. She found that she had been churning at her drink with her straw without realising it, and she looked at Gary with some wryness as he patiently repeated his question. 'Yes, and while you're in the restroom, wash that face of yours! I can hardly tell who's underneath all that ice-cream!'

He slid from his seat and, still clutching his unassembled kite, edged around some people and made for the back of the small restaurant. Janie had finished her ice-cream and was busy looking at her book. Devan watched her for some time in a vague, thoughtful way. She felt again that stirring of her dormant sexuality, and was deeply disturbed. She heaved a sigh and was barely aware of it coming out as a groan. No. This couldn't, shouldn't be happening to her. She wasn't ready, wasn't prepared. Ryan was right. He could see so much of her, so accurately. She was a creature of intensity and emotion, and when she felt, she felt deeply. This dawning of physical awareness couldn't happen, not between her and Ryan. He had the potential of seeing too deeply into her, and if she gave in to her feelings, she could be lost for ever.

Her hand clenched into a fist as it lay on the cool table surface. She knew instinctively that she might have the power to hurt him, that keenly intelligent, sensitive, forceful man. She knew that he wasn't looking for the kind of relationship she had suddenly, vividly imagined between them. He was looking to help her as a friend, an editor, one caring human being to another. She shouldn't want even that.

But his simple, nagging concern had touched her deeper than anything else had touched her for a long time. His careful treatment of her was making her stealthily, sneakily grateful. His persistence was beginning to wear at her, as her breakdown into tears that very morning had revealed. His stubborn faith was weighing her down with the burden of another's expectations—useless, pressuring expectations. She knew she couldn't begin to give him what he wanted in the first place, so she had no right to expect him to give her any more of himself.

After a time, she came to herself and the realisation that her drink was now nothing more than a melted dilution of ice and weak lemonade. She pushed it away with a grimace, and looked around. Janie was absorbedly reading. Gary was nowhere to be seen.

Devan turned and looked up, then down, the aisle. She couldn't see her nephew's blond head anywhere. She turned and nudged her niece, 'Janie.' Janie grunted. 'Janie! Have you seen Gary come out of the men's restroom?'

Janie's freckled face screwed into a brief frown, and she looked around. Then she went back to her book with supreme indifference. 'Nope.'

Devan began to feel alarmed. She slid from the booth, told Janie to stay put, and made her way to the back of the restaurant. No Gary in sight. She found the men's toilet and knocked, tentatively. When nobody answered, she pushed the door open gingerly. A man was standing just in front of the sink, zipping up his trousers, and he looked up with a startled, angry expression. Devan went scarlet, and ducked out again. She called through the door, 'Is there a blond boy inside, about six years old?'

The door was yanked open; it was the man, now looking quite amused, which made her redden even more. 'Sorry, lady,' he said, and passed her by.

The man's response made her forget her embarrassment, and she looked around her in real bafflement, and alarm. There was no way to exit from the back of the small restaurant. Surely that would mean it would be impossible for anyone to take Gary without her knowledge. Her eyes suddenly narrowed. She had been so preoccupied, and Janie had been quite intent on her reading. It would have been impossible for someone to take a protesting Gary past her, but it wouldn't have been impossible for Gary to sneak silently past. And he had been clutching his kite.

She started to head grimly back to the booth, intending to get Janie and go and search for her brat of a nephew, when something flashed by the huge picture windows of the delicatessen and made her stop stock still in surprise.

How Gary had managed to put the kite together without help was beyond her, but that he had was more than apparent as he streaked by with it fluttering, huge and black behind him. Her open mouth shut with a furious and audible snap. 'Janie!' she barked, making the girl jump a mile. 'Get your stuff. We're going.'

Devan flew out of the door and turned sharply in the direction she'd seen Gary sprinting. As soon as she caught sight of the kite, which looked like a giant black moth, she roared for Gary to stop if he valued his life, and she sprinted down the pavement.

Gary had been flying the kite on a very short lead, but when he heard his aunt's wrathful voice, he promptly dropped the ball of twine, which rolled along the ground. The day had been windy in gusty spurts, and the kite suddenly shot up, the string slipping completely from his lax hands. Devan watched as he scrambled after it, but the rolling, bouncing ball of twine managed to elude him. She was gaining on him, but not fast enough, as the wind took the kite and blew it right into one of the town's four traffic lights. The string tangled in the crossbar which held the swinging lights, and the kite rose in altitude, flying twenty feet above the street like a flag. The twine rolled merrily along, right into the path of an oncoming car, which ran right over it. Gary had skidded to a halt at the street and was looking on, horrified at the fate of his beloved kite. Devan caught up with him just as the string snagged on the passing car's front bumper. They both held their breath as the line pulled taut, and then the kite was yanked free of the pole. Janie then joined them both, in time to watch with the other two as the car, the unsuspecting driver, and the kite flying along behind disappeared in the distance. After staring from her fascinated, open-mouthed nephew to the black fluttering speck in the distance, Devan's anger suddenly evaporated, and she threw back her head to laugh until she cried.

* * *

It took careful negotiation to pull around Ryan's rented car, but Devan manged that with more ease than she had managed to back out. The dilapidated garage door was still left open, so she drew smoothly in and switched off the engine. Total silence reigned in the car. 'Right,' she said, sternly, and opened her door. 'Come on, you two.'

Janie and Gary followed along behind her, Gary's steps lagging quite noticeably. They trooped in the back door and found Helen serenely cleaning out the refrigerator. She looked up with a smile as they entered. 'How'd everything go?' she asked, glancing to Devan, who stood in eloquent silence. Helen's face then changed, and she stood to brush off her knees. 'All right, what happened?'

Devan reached back and grabbed Gary's shoulder as he started to slink away. She thrust her nephew forward, and said grimly, though her eyes were twinkling, 'I think he should be the one to tell you.'

Gary swallowed and said hollowly, 'All of it?'

'All of it.' Devan headed for her library with her purchases, longing for peace. 'And Janie, you make sure he tells the truth.' She stopped at the doorway, and turned. 'And I'll tell you this,' she said succinctly. 'Never again will I take you horrible brats anywhere.'

'That's what you said the last time,' said Janie.

Devan's lips twitched before she pulled them into severity. 'This time,' she stated with dignity, 'I really mean it.'

She went to the privacy of her library and sank

into her armchair with a heartfelt sigh. Much as she acted the part of a disapproving aunt, everyone knew it to be an act, for she tremendously enjoyed her niece and nephew. But they were exhausting, and she was feeling distinctly limp. After a bit, she drew out her new books and looked them over with interest. Then she made room for them on her shelves.

She wondered where Ryan was, but didn't especially want to backtrack to the kitchen to ask Helen, as she rather suspected that Gary's crimes were still being judged, and punishment for his disobedience being meted out. She headed for the stairs, intending to put her bag away in her room. Paris greeted her, stretched across the bottom stair, and she bent to pat his head before stepping over him. As she reached the first floor, she heard nothing but silence. All the lights were off in the light of day, and she glanced into the open door of the guest room.

Then she stopped. A dark form was stretched out, fully clothed, on the top of the bedcovers. Her fingers loosened on the strap of her bag and let it slide gently to the floor by the door as she looked at Ryan. The sight of him drew her footsteps, slow and quiet and reluctant. She stood by the bed, looking down. He was big, even lying down, his long legs stretched comfortably out, one arm flexed back, the hand tucked under his pillow. His head was turned away from her, his face smoothed, his well-cut hair tousled. Big, and solid, and definitely masculine, from the line of his hips and the length

of his legs to the bulk and power of his shoulders
and chest. She noted that he was freshly dressed,
and that the shadow of his beard was shaved clean.
His hair fell forward on his temple, and she saw her
hand go out very carefully. The way he had held
her that morning, tight and bruisingly, for he had
cared about her hurting. The way he had held her.

Her fingers very lightly touched at his temple,
feeling the warm skin and hair, and then she gently
brushed the hair back. And without warning, he
turned to look silently up at her.

For he wasn't asleep.

Her hand jerked back as if burned, her face
flooding with an appalled realisation, even as his
own came vividly alive, his light eyes leaping. For
he wasn't asleep when she had thought he was, and
everything had been in her face in that one instant:
the regret, the uncertainty, the naked yearning and
new flooding tenderness.

Naked.

Her face settled into stony lines in rejection of
both her own feelings and his swift dawn of
understanding, and she stepped back, turning
away. 'When do you go back?' she asked, a
deliberate effort to make him remember the
transient position he held in her life, and the fact
that he would soon be leaving.

'I took two weeks,' he said, shifting on the bed.
He stood up.

His reply could have meant anything. It wasn't
necessarily a direct response to her question, she
realised, but she couldn't stay to think of it, as she

heard his light footsteps coming her way. She panicked as she thought, an awful feeling in the pit of her stomach, of how unguarded her face had been to his penetrating gaze. She bolted for the door, and knew even as she did it that she had reacted in the most foolish way possible, for she already knew that he was quicker, stronger, and he wasn't about to let her get away. And sure enough, he had hold of her and dragged her around to face him.

She gave it another shot. 'What the hell are you doing?' she asked, her face, body, voice quite cold.

He didn't even bother to respond, his entire body tight with something, his light eyes intent on her expression, her lips. And it scared her half to death, for he had indeed read the yearnings in her expression correctly, and that intentness had sexuality dark at its back, and determination. He let out his breath slowly, carefully, and then took another in.

And dropped his mouth on her like a stone: hard, crushing, brooking none of her resistance or her rejection, her repelling manner. He did it with a silent concentration that was completely unnerving, because he was doing it as though he wanted nothing more than to do it, to move his lips roughly on hers in an effort to penetrate deep, hauling her close against him.

It wasn't at all like that morning had been. It was worse, it was terrible, it was far better than that morning had been. It was him pushing between her lips, it was her, opening with a sudden shudder,

kissing him back. It was his sharp intake of breath
at her response as she gave in and slid her hands up
the bulk of his upper arms to sink her fingers deep
into his hair as he bent her back.

And he was swamping her, overwhelming,
making her lose her reason. This time it was she
who said, pleadingly, 'Stop!' as she dragged her
mouth away from him.

Of course he didn't listen; why should he, when
she had forgotten to make her hands loosen from
his hair, when she was still holding him urgently?
His head angled down as he bent her back further,
and he nuzzled underneath her hair to kiss her
neck, and then to suck gently at the pulse beating
at her ear.

She surprised herself as much as he when she
wrenched away. She nearly fell as she tripped
when she left the enclosing circle of his arms, but
she caught herself up, breathing heavily. She
raised her hands to push her hair off her hot
forehead, and her fingers clenched. She was going
crazy, crazy to have lost her resolution so quickly
and so easily. Don't get involved with him; don't
get near.

She nearly jumped out of her skin when his arms
came underneath hers, wrapping her close to him
again, his chest against her back, his hands flat on
her slim ribcage. His hips against her buttocks.
Heat coursed through her, and she cursed at it
viciously, and then Ryan said in her ear softly, his
warm breath tickling, 'I think I'm now beginning
to understand. It's not what, but who. It's not

something that happened to you, but someone who hurt you. That's the beginning of it, isn't it, when you broke down and couldn't write? That's why you leap like a scalded cat whenever I try to get near, to get beneath that resistant façade you erect. What did he do to you? Who is he?'

Tension had quivered through her in many layers, physical and mental, and, when he pressed a featherlight kiss to the sensitive tip of her ear, it snapped, making her sag against his chest, her head falling sideways to his shoulder. He bent further and she felt lips again on her exposed neck. She shrank from it. 'Don't!'

'Why?' he muttered, biting her skin in a delicate nip, making her shake her head violently. 'You're starved for simple human contact, and I do so want to touch you——'

'*Stop it*!' The words came out of her in a hiss as she dragged away, knowing bitterly all the while that it was only because he chose to let her go. She whirled to face him, her body trembling, her face flushed hot. 'Don't you touch me again, do you hear? Don't you touch me again!'

'Hiya,' said Janic conversationally from the open dorway. Devan leapt as though struck, and spun to the doorway, the expression in her eyes blinded. 'Sorry, didn't mean to scare you. What's up? Wanna play a game?'

Devan tried desperately to get hold of her racing, pounding pulse and breath, realising by Janie's calm demeanour that the girl hadn't really grasped the implications of the tension that vibrated between herself and Ryan. 'No,' she said then, shortly, amazed to hear the unsteadiness in her voice. She shot a glance to Ryan. 'No, I don't want to play any game.'

His lids came down over his light eyes, making him seem lazy and insolent. He studied her almost dispassionately, and she turned and stalked from his room, making for hers as fast as she could. Then—and it would have unsettled her very much indeed had she seen it—he smiled.

CHAPTER SEVEN

DEVAN rushed inside her room and both shut and locked the door. Then she fell on to her bed and would have wept a storm, except that she was too stunned and frightened of both herself and of him, and of everything that was pulsing to painful life inside of her. This couldn't be allowed. She had to get rid of him and count herself lucky to have done it.

She pushed herself off her bed with the force of her teeming, racing thoughts, and then stumbled to her cupboard to draw out her electric typewriter. She dragged it to the door, which she unlocked clumsily, and she clumped down the stairs with it. At the dining room table, she hoisted it up, took the typewriter out of its case, and plugged it in. She raced back up the stairs to scrabble for paper, ribbon, and pencils, and then fell back down to the ground floor, throwing the supplies on to the table in a scatter.

The noise she was making drew everyone's attention, and they came from the various parts of the house to stare at her. She ignored them, and was unaware of the puzzled, disconcerted frown that had fallen between Ryan's level brows, or of Helen's concern. With practised fingers, she clipped a ribbon cartridge into place, turned on the typewriter, and threaded paper into the carriage.

Janie and Gary lost interest and drifted away. Ryan said very evenly, 'Just what do you think you're doing?'

She jumped, and looked up at him. She said through her teeth, 'I'm proving a point.' Heavy, numbing pain ran in her for the futility of uselessly trying what she knew she couldn't do. She was barren inside, and she couldn't bear it.

'Why are you hurting yourself this way?' he asked, gently. 'It's too soon to expect anything like a real effort from yourself. Give yourself time——'

She cried through his words, 'I'm going to prove to you that it's really gone, so that you'll go away and leave me alone! There'll be nothing to keep you here any more——'

Helen made a sudden movement. Ryan looked to her and slightly shook his head. He then turned his gaze to Devan, pityingly. 'Prove what you will,' he replied quietly, and left the room.

She put her hands to her face and searched dully for meaning to put to words, and found nothing to say. The early afternoon faded to early evening. She tried several times, and ended with tearing the paper from the carriage, wadding it viciously, and throwing it hard with a fling of her arm. Ryan came to the doorway several times from the kitchen, but she never saw him, and he went away again. She looked for themes, rough ideas, for anything to build on, and couldn't sweat out a single thing.

She was brilliant; she was bright. She was nothing.

Everything she had become was wrapped up in her writing. A lonely child and adolescent, she had been paralysed by a cocoon of shyness. Helen and her books had been her only friends, and she had learned to devour stories with greed. They had been her source of enjoyment and fulfilment, the way she had learned about other ways of life. Their mother had died early in Devan's life; their father had worked very hard at trying to forget, and one of the things he had tried to forget was his children.

Helen had survived well enough. She'd been slightly older, and graced with a serenity of the soul that drew friends to her like bees homing to honey. Devan's personality had smouldered within her crippling cocoon, and she had become determined that no one would forget or ignore her again. She was going to be so good, so aggressive, so bright and ambitious; she was going to reach out and awe others with the sparkling enchantment of her wit and wile. She would communicate in the only way she knew how; she realised that, even as a teenager. And so, with burning eyes and a silent, burning determination, she graduated from high school, and blazed through college to attain her goal.

Everything had been within her sights. Everything had been within her grasp. She'd had a handsome, intelligent lover, she'd had a consuming career, she'd had her youth and health. But Lee had brought it all down around her, had pulled her air castles to shreds, and she had known then how useless it all was.

All of it. All her conviction, all her insight was false. She—what did she know of relationships, of deep, hidden motivations, of real life characters? She was a failure at real life, a failure at healthy relationships. She couldn't keep her father's love, and she couldn't keep Lee's. How could she have the colossal arrogance to believe that she could ever write the reality of anything when she couldn't live it?

She couldn't believe.

Bitterness welled up, and with a violent sweep of her arms, she thrust the typewriter away from herself and on to the floor. The machine broke into splinters. The crash of it resounded in the downstairs rooms, and she heard a dim echo of it shriek up the stairs and bounce off the first floor walls.

Then there was a concerted rush, and Ryan was in the dining room, standing stiff and tense in front of her, his eyes running over the broken machine, the wadded pieces of paper, the scatter of materials over the table. Gary had appeared from the living room, Janie was behind Ryan, and Helen behind Janie. Ryan leaned over and put his hands on the table. 'When will you stop tormenting yourself?' he asked in a low voice.

She pushed herself away from the table, her slim body taut and trembling, her hands clenching and unclenching. 'There,' she said hoarsely, viciously. 'You've got your answer. Shut the door on your

way out.' She kicked the keyboard of the typewriter from her path and heard it skitter along the
floor, and then she strode for the front of the house.

Helen said, quickly and quietly, 'Kids, come on.
Help me get supper started.'

'I wanna watch,' said Gary.

That was all Devan heard, though there was a
sudden scurry, and a quickly bitten off squawk
from her nephew. She went to the front window in
the living room and looked outside stonily. She
heard slow, quiet footsteps approaching, and she
refused to turn around. She had done it this time,
she really had. No one would stay after having put
up with what he had in the last few days. This was
it.

'I'm not going,' he said.

Incredulity held her immobile for a pulsing
second. Then she whirled. He looked fresh and
alert, although tired lines ran in deepened paths
from his nostrils to the sides of his mouth. He was
regarding her patiently. 'What do you mean, you're
not going? You've got to; I'm not attempting to
write any more——'

'Damn the writing,' he said carelessly.

He was leaning against the open archway, his
arms crossed over his chest, his gaze steady on her,
his face now expressionless. She felt her heart give
a great thump at his words, and she groped over to
sit on the sofa, her eyes huge in her face as she
stared at him. She repeated, parrot-like, 'Damn
. . . the writing . . .?'

'Yes. What the hell do I care if you never write

another word?' he replied, with a shrug.

Her brow wrinkled in slow confusion. 'But——'
she stammered, while at the back of her mind she
realised that he had done it to her again, screwed
up her reason, upset her understanding, 'but, the
whole reason you stayed was—was the writing.
Wasn't it?'

'I'd made up my mind to stay on a misunderstan-
ding,' he said calmly, while his eyes watched her
closely. 'I thought the writing was the cause of your
unhappiness. The real situation is that your
unhappiness is the reason why you cannot write.'

'You're basing that on supposition!' she flared,
her hands in fists. 'The real situation is that you
don't know what the hell you're talking about!'

'Got another explanation you'd care to share?'
he asked, sardonically. She didn't answer, so he
went on, 'What do you think I want? You seem to
think I have this God-like image of myself righting
all your woes and then leaving you to your happy
ending! I came here on a professional basis, to see
if there was anything I could do to help you in your
work. I'm staying because I've come to care about
you as a person. What is it, Devan, have you come
to see your writing as the equivalent of your own
worth? Sure, you're good, you're possibly great.
Who cares? The world will be here tomorrow if you
don't write that bestseller you were harping on
about. Someone else will make the *New York Times*
top ten list. Why can't you just try to be content
with whatever you are, or are not doing? So what if

you can't drag any themes out of your head. Forget about it!'

She put her hands to her forehead in confusion. He didn't know the whole situation, couldn't know enough to speak accurately. Why did what he was saying affect her so? 'But I need it,' she said, on a moan.

While she had been overwhelmed by an inner turbulence, he had pushed away from the staircase to walk over to her. He sat beside her on the couch, and grasped one of her hands to pull it down and cradle it. 'Why?' he asked gently. 'Why that badly?'

She turned her head to look at him, weary truth at the back of her brown eyes. At his waiting, intent face, she bent her head. 'It's my line. It's how I reach people.' Her hand moved in his grasp. 'It's how I tell what I am.'

Awareness was dawning in those grey-blue eyes. He then said slowly, 'You reach people, you communicate, you touch, through your books. You feel bereft without it.' His face gentled amazingly. She had glanced back at him, and her eyes clung to that look in wide-eyed fascination. 'Devan, there are countless ways to communicate. Even silently: a touch, a look, a smile.' His hand reached for her head and stroked, and she quivered throughout her body.

Her eyes fluttered shut, her mouth trembled, and she had to turn her face away to hide it. 'But I— can't——' she said, strangled. 'I can't seem to communicate well enough, I——'

'Good God, do you actually believe that?' he asked, astonished. 'How could you be so wrong? What about your close relationship with Helen?'

'Helen,' said Devan, with difficulty, 'could make a heart of stone love her well.'

In spite of himself, he smiled. 'She could at that. But what about the kids? I've seen how you treat them, how you tease and pretend to be stern. But your love shows very clearly in it all, and they know it. That's why they're always flocking around you, and wanting to be with you. As for myself, I've been more than able to pick up your emotions very well, ever since I got here. Lady—you radiate!'

She stared at him, completely bewildered, at a loss, uncomprehending. Suddenly she was very tired, and longing for bed. His eyes, searching her face; his face looking hard, reassuring, supportive. She said then, very quietly, 'I don't understand anything any more.'

'And there's a lot more I'd like to understand about you, Devan Richardson.' Her eyes asked him silently what he meant by that, but he just shook his head with a smile. 'We'll talk later, all right? Right now, Helen and I were fixing supper, and it should be about ready.'

Her face changed swiftly, amusement running over her delicately etched features. She groaned, 'Oh, Lord, more food! Just skip it, OK? I'm not——'

'Hungry. Yes, I know,' he said drily, as he began to smile. 'But we've all eaten lunch, and you haven't. You are definitely having supper.'

'I'll bet you're as autocratic at work, too,' she muttered, ostensibly grumpy. But a small smile touched at her lips.

He wrapped a lazy, loose arm around her shoulders and pulled her close, and for a heart-stopping moment she thought he was going to kiss her. But he didn't, merely rubbing lightly at her smaller nose with his as he told her, indulgently, 'Always. But it's not as fun. They rarely argue back like you.'

A vivid grin splashed over her features. Then she said, composedly, 'Somebody's got to put you in your place.'

They wandered through the dining room, wading through the mess Devan had created, and into the kitchen. She was secretly amazed at how good he had managed to make her feel after her bitter and passionate outburst. They both found the children putting the finishing touches to the table while Helen worked at the counter, and, suddenly filled with remorse, Devan walked over to her sister and put her chin over Helen's shoulder. 'Hi,' she said. 'Sorry about the mess in the dining room, I'll clean it up right away.'

'No problem,' said Helen, with a smile.

'I'm also sorry I haven't been much help these last few days,' continued Devan, purging her soul.

Her sister gave her a damp pat on the cheek. 'You've had a lot on your mind, and you haven't been feeling well.'

Paris galloped from nowhere, and with a magnificent bound landed in the midst of the

plates and cutlery. It didn't ruffle Gary in the
slightest, but Janie yowled, and started beating on
the cat's back with a rolled up napkin, which sent
him leaping away again. The minor ruckus had
attracted the attention of the three adults, and,
while Devan frankly laughed, Helen just sighed
and said, 'All right. Clear the dishes, and set the
table with clean things.'

Blinking with astonishment, Gary looked from
the table to his exasperating mother. 'But it's not
dirty!'

'There is no telling from where that beast just
came. Reset the table,' ordered Helen implacably.
With a grumble, they complied, and Ryan pitched
in to lighten their spirits. Devan just watched for a
moment and after asking her sister if there was
anything she could do to help, and receiving a
negative, she picked up the rubbish bin and went
to the dining room to clear away the worst of the
mess.

While she scrambled under the table for
crumpled papers and bits of ruined machinery, she
fell to brooding. It seemed that she hadn't acted at
all like herself today, with Ryan. What had got into
her, to rush from his room just because he had
made a simple pass at her? And to then throw what
was essentially the equivalent of a temper tantrum
and wreck a perfectly good machine was unforgi-
vable. This wasn't like her at all. She was the quick
one, always good at quips and snappy returns,
always able to handle conversation with at least the
appearance of composure. Even with Lee she had

been able to appear unflappable if she so wished.

Ryan had the irritating, disturbing, alarming, exciting habit of wrecking her composure completely. She thought about that worriedly. She finally came to the conclusion that it was merely that he had caught her on a low ebb, with her defences down. She told herself that she actually believed it, but if that were so, it didn't explain why she worried around until suppertime.

The aromatic smells wafting to her nose told her that Helen had prepared her speciality, a garlic, lemon and honey sauce over pork chops. When Devan had peered over her shoulder, she had been busy with mashing potatoes, and a fresh batch of crusty blueberry muffins had been cooling o
n the worktop. Devan's mouth began to water in anticipation, and she registered that fact with some dryness. Helen was traditionally the cook, while Devan washed up afterwards, for her sister found cooking a soothing and comforting pastime. She especially liked to cook for other people, whereas Devan barely took the time to make food edible. Her mouth twisted in self-mockery. Domestic skills were not in her array of talents.

She was under the table, sitting down while she juggled a piece of typewriter in her hands. Ryan's head popped into sight as he bent down to look at her.

'Such a face,' he said, mildly.

She spun around on her hands and knees and practically screamed at him, 'Don't *startle* me so!'

Astonishment flared in his upside down expression, and then vivid laughter as she leaned against the legs of a chair and pressed a hand to her racing heart. The children peered briefly around the corner and giggled.

After a moment, he said, his voice laced with amusement, 'I wasn't deliberately trying to sneak up on you.' She shook her head and snorted, and then started to crawl out from under the table. 'You're as sensitive and as jumpy as a cat, aren't you?'

Her hands slapped on the floor; when she had cleared the table, he reached down a lazy hand and hoisted her to her feet effortlessly. 'I guess I am,' she then said, ruefully. 'Thank heavens Helen never complains; Lee always did.'

He said, very softly, his eyes bright and shrewd, 'I was right, then.' Her head snapped up from inspecting her dirty hands, and her eyes widened with the knowledge of what she had just confessed without realising it.

She stalked for the bathroom to wash for supper, and threw over her shoulder, 'You don't know what you're talking about.'

He came and leaned against the open doorpost while he watched her scrub fiercely at her hands with the bar of soap. 'Your favourite response,' he said drily, with more than a hint of anger. 'If I'm always so wrong, why don't you take the time to correct me? But you never do, you just press your lips together with that God-awful stubbornness.

What is it with you, a defence mechanism? What are you trying to hide?'

Truth slammed in on her, and her hands stilled under rushing water. Her expression grew perplexed, her body quite quiet as her thoughts raced. Why was she so reticent about Lee? Was it that she didn't want Ryan or Helen to know of her past failures? Was it that she found Lee too painful to discuss? What was she trying to hide? Pulsebeat, moments passing by, her breathing suspended. 'I don't know,' she said, at last.

He then said, in a measured tone, 'I lost my temper. I apologise. I shouldn't have pried.'

And suddenly she was laughing as she whirled to face him. She threw her wet hands to her hips, seeing his brows shoot up in response. He was at his ease against the post, long legs angled, lean hips slouching, his arms indolently crossed at his wide chest. She demanded, 'What is it with you, anyway? I get the distinct impression you've been trying to treat me with kid gloves; you're so meticulously careful about what you say sometimes! Tell me, really. Are you that way with everyone?'

His eyes lit up, and he started to smile. 'Actually,' he said, 'no. They tell me I'm quite a roaring slavedriver at work. I don't know about that. There are simply some things I do not allow.' Looking at him and seeing all over again that square jaw and that determined, straight mouth, she could well believe it. His expression grew rueful. 'You've been on shaky ground,' he said then. 'I didn't want to hurt you.'

She blinked, and looked down at her hands, as if noticing their dampness for the first time. She rubbed them together. 'And I've reacted abominably,' she said quietly. 'I apologise,' She glanced up, lightning-quick. He was regarding her with the strangest expression: understanding, even tender. He inclined his head to her, and she smiled.

Helen called from the kitchen, 'For heaven's sake, will you two come on? Supper's on the table and getting cold!'

Ryan laughed as Devan scurried to dry her hands with a towel, and they were soon sitting down to eat. Devan had to grin at how very homely it all was. Gary was drumming his heels against his chair legs and blowing bubbles in his milk with a striped straw. Janie had brought her book to the table. Helen passed to Ryan, who was sitting to Devan's left, a large bowl of the fluffy mashed potatoes which had a dollop of butter melting in the middle. They were eating off mismatched plates; Devan's had a chip on the edge of it. There were no pretensions to elegance or sophistication, no formalities, just a well-cooked meal and all of them sharing it, like one big happy family. She reached out and picked up her drink, grinning as she looked down at it. Drinking milk, for God's sake!

Ryan had helped himself to the potatoes and passed the bowl to her, which she started to pass by without taking any. His firm grip on her forearm stopped her. He reached over and slapped a substantial spoonful on to her plate. 'And like it, too.'

Janie and Gary watched with bright eyes. Devan took a deep breath, and then let it blow out with a laugh.

Ryan was grinning lopsidedly, and he said around a bite of pork chop, 'Like to share the joke?'

His light eyes were smiling. He expressed a lot with those eyes, even when he wore an overtly impassive face. She looked around, to Helen's interested, amused attention, to Gary and Janie, and to Paris blinking distantly at the scene which disguised an avid interest in the meal. She salted her potatoes. 'Nope,' she replied.

For a big man, Ryan held himself neatly, and knew when to be still. His hands wielded his fork and knife with delicacy. While Devan dawdled with her food, he finished his meal, and then sat back to talk lazily with Helen. Sometimes he would turn to the children and comment to them. He didn't talk down and his manner was frank, to which they responded remarkably well. Their table manners were the best that Devan had ever seen from them.

She managed to finish most of what was on her plate, and when she finally felt the protest of tight stomach muscles, she silently picked up her plate and handed it over to Ryan, who took it with a quick look and a grin. The muffins were deposited on the table, and she couldn't resist taking one and buttering it lavishly, then nibbling at it until she thought her stomach would burst. The outside was crunchy hard and the inside moist and steaming, and bursting with sweet fruit. It was delicious and she wanted to finish it, but ended up handing over half to Ryan.

After supper, the children disappeared as if by magic, and Helen went to put up her feet in the living room and watch television. Devan finally rose from the table and began to stack things together absently. She barely glanced at Ryan as he, too, stood and started to help. She started running the dishwater, and let the steamy hot water rush over her hands to turn them red as her thoughts went back. She said quietly, 'You seem to fit in well here.'

He gave her a swift smile as he stacked the plates by the sink. 'Are you surprised?'

She tilted her head as she watched soapsuds explode into frothy existence. 'A little,' she admitted. 'I'm not sure what I expected you to be like, but somehow this pleasant helpfulness wasn't it.'

After a moment, he said lightly, 'I'm not sure I like the impression you had of me.'

She made a disclaiming gesture, and soapsuds flew. 'I didn't mean anything bad by that—I think you just weren't a real person to me before. You were just a signature and a set of observations.' She took the glasses and started to scrub at the rims.

Her hair swung forward when her head was bent, and she felt his hand touch at her cheek and then gently tuck it back behind her ear. 'And how do you see me now?' he asked.

Her hands stilled. 'You're a frustrating, exasperating, irritating, wholly likeable man,' she said softly, and a slight smile touched at her lips, softening her face. His hand went to her back, trailed down her spine, and rested to rub lightly at the back of her waist as she bent over the sink.

'At least we seem to be getting along better,' he murmured. 'You aren't throwing water on my head any more.'

Her mouth straightened, and a trace of grimness crept into her voice. She said briefly, 'A week ago, I would have said it was impossible.' Then, with difficulty, 'I'm not too keen on starting relationships right now.'

He laughed, low and deep in his chest, standing just by her and slightly behind, a large tangible presence. 'I could have told you that,' he replied drily.

The back door was open, the night humming with insects. She looked out through the blackness of the rectangular screen door and could see nothing of the lawn. Then she felt her heart quicken, her hands actually tremble. She clasped them together and felt her fingers slip wetly on each other. She said in a low voice, 'I met Lee when I was twenty-six. It was a—rather long-standing relationship.'

Startled, he froze and she sensed him turning to stare at her, trying to gauge the importance of what she was saying. 'Romantic?' he said, the flat word a question.

She tried to shrug lightly, and at least managed the shrug. 'We were lovers, if that's what you mean,' she said baldly. How would he take that? 'We were, I guess, much like any other couple. We lived together in a rather cramped apartment. I was sure we would get married one day, but somehow there didn't seem to be any hurry. Looking back, I suppose the trouble started when I began to work on my first novel, but I didn't realise it at the time. I thought we were just going through a rough period like everyone does now and then, and I never doubted that things would change. Then one morning, he packed his clothes and—left.'

She was hot suddenly, with an onrush of blood to her face. Her teeth clenched, her mouth pulled taut, lines on either side. Her hands were bone-white and red as she gripped them together.

She glanced to her left, up at his face, and his expression was totally, carefully—too carefully—blank. His eyes were shuttered as he looked down at the worktop in front of him. 'Why did he leave?'

Intense frustration. 'I don't know.'

Sudden weariness, showing through that blank façade. He didn't believe her. 'I see.'

She spoke through her stiff lips, for she found she couldn't bear that weary look, 'No, I don't think you do.' His eyes flashed quickly up, blazing hot, and that look burned deep into her. Then it was gone, as he saw the sincerity in hers. 'If what you said earlier was true, I don't understand. You see, he told me he couldn't take it any more. He said that I was too distant, too wrapped up in my work. He said that he had tried to have p-patience, tried to wait for a change, but it hadn't come, and that was why he was leaving. He s-said that I wasn't prepared to give or show enough in our relationship, and that maybe he had expected too much, but it was too late anyway. He said he wasn't coming back, and he didn't.'

She had tried to speak plainly and calmly, but the pain was still there from that last awful scene. When she saw how Ryan's eyes had begun to blaze again at her stuttered words, she flushed hot with agitation and turned to stare with wide, stricken eyes at the white refrigerator, biting viciously at her lips.

'No warning?' he asked.

Her jaw muscle bunched, the spasm marring the slim sleek line of her cheek. 'Just like that.'

'That bastard,' he said thinly.

Her head jerked around. 'He had to have a reason,' she sighed, upset and confusion painfully evident in her voice. 'There had to have been— something in what he said. He was a reasonable man. He always made cautious decisions. At first I was stunned and angry, but-but I couldn't make any other sense out of it all——'

He surged from the worktop, stalked across the kitchen and then back again. 'I don't buy it,' he said flatly, and for some reason he was furious. She knew it, could see it in every taut line of his big body, but she couldn't make sense of that either, and she was very weary of her incomprehension.

She took the hand towel and wiped her hands dry, and then just bent her head and hid her face. 'I just don't buy it, Devan. He could have left you with something. He could have left without a word of explanation, and it would have hurt, but you would have got over it. Instead, he takes the time and effort to tear your confidence to shreds.'

'No!' she whispered, appalled. Three years, and her own commitment to the relationship that had been a marriage in all but name. At least, that's what she had thought it was. Had Lee felt differently? She said, more strongly, 'No! He couldn't have done that—he cared about me!'

He whipped around, lightning quick. 'You're still hung up on the guy, aren't you?' he snarled, and his face was frightening to behold. 'You're still pining away for the son of a bitch! Why are you so *blind* to what he did to you?'

'I'm not!' she shouted, pushing away from the worktop and stumbling. 'I'm not, but there had to be a reason for it; it wasn't a senseless occurrence, can't you see that?'

He jerked over to the sink and started to wash the dishes, piling things into the sink roughly as he ran some rinsing water, and she distinctly heard something break. Then he just put his hands on the edge of the worktop, bent his head and shook it from side to side. 'I can't see anything straight,' he bit out.

She turned and walked out of the house. Numbness descended on her as she took great breaths of the outside fresh air, but it wasn't enough to dull the hurting. It was just enough to keep her from thinking any more, for she had exhausted the endless search for answers, reviving old arguments, old scenes, old conflicts until they were worn thin in her mind. No use thinking about it, no use any of it, no use thinking. That was a litany she had come to recognise. She ducked her head and strolled, feet shuffling through the grass, through the back garden and to the path that led to the nearby clearing.

The light from the house shone out from the windows and the back door. She thought about going back and helping him clean up the supper mess, but she couldn't bear to be close to him and his inexplicable, intense reaction to what she'd told him. He was another one she couldn't understand, and her faith in her own perceptions was as shaky as it had ever been.

Perhaps she could go back inside and play a game with the children. Or maybe watch television with Helen, like they had so many times in the last year. But her heart wasn't in anything, and she couldn't even bring herself to go back to the house, to her room. The dark solitude soothed her as she reached the clearing and threw herself on the thick cushion of grass. She curled on her side, her knees tucked up, and she listened to the orchestrated night song vibrating from the bushes.

Something came to her, a quote she had always loved of Robert Herrick's. She whispered it gently to the shadows; "'Gather ye rosebuds while ye may, Old Time is still aflying, And this same flower, that smiles to-day, To-morrow will be dying.'"

Brief life, inconstancy, fragile dreams and hopes, and the flame of ambition she had so delicately fostered. But the fire dies, and the fleeting flame-flower, so moving and lovely, fades to dark ash. Nothing lasts, so nothing matters, and she had simply to take that lesson to heart.

The problem was that her heart wasn't in it.

CHAPTER EIGHT

PURPLE washed over Devan's mind in a dark serenity. She fell into a lulled, mindless state, feeling her cheek lie on crushed scented grass, feeling the uptwist of a tree root digging into her side. Then the awareness of another presence came to her in the hint of movement, in the rustle of quiet footsteps under the sound of night. She refused to lift her head, keeping turned away as she willed whoever it was to leave. But she was practising a little delusion on herself; she knew that it was Ryan standing behind her all the time, and she grew rigid with the silence of his throbbing tension.

The she felt rather than heard the sensation of him coming towards her and coming fast. It frightened her into looking up, shrinking down, her heart giving a great leap. Ryan's large, silhouetted body filled her vision. She struggled to push herself up from her lying position.

But then she couldn't do anything, couldn't move, couldn't even cry out, for he had reached down with his two strong hands and yanked her by the shoulders, just hauled her right up against him. His hand snaked to the back of her head while his own came down. His lips were blurred in shadow and distorted as he snarled very quietly into her ear, 'You're still thinking of him, aren't you, lying here in the dark? You're still grieving; he meant that much to you——'

He was breathing heavily and hard, his body tight and vibrating. She couldn't move, for this had been too unexpected, and her hands gripped uselessly at his shirt, his waist. She was off balance and afraid, for her heart was beginning to pound in slow, hard slugs. 'No!' she exclaimed, making a sound as his hand tightened in her hair. 'I was just tired——'

He wasn't listening, and her words faltered to a stunned silence as he turned his head and started to nuzzle hungrily at her neck. Her eyes caught a shadowed impression of his powerful shoulders hunching over her as he knelt by her side, and of the lighter overhead branches swaying over his black head. Then his mouth was slanting across her cheekbone, over to her lips, crushing them and pushing them open as he thrust in deeply with his tongue. Devan moaned, for she was frightened and couldn't move, with his fist in her hair and holding her immobile, his body holding her off balance, her hands clenching and unclenching in his shirt, against his body. She was frightened, not of him, but of herself, for hotness bolted along her torso, leaping in her loins; he was igniting a fire in her. His head reared back, his chest heaving in a harsh intake of breath, his light eyes glittering in the darkness that was his face. They raked over her, her swollen mouth, her huge and dilated, moon-filled eyes. Then he said, on a low growl, 'I can make you forget him.'

But even as he spoke, Devan's hands were creeping up jerkily, along the front of his chest. She knew because she saw them, and was as much shocked by that as she was by anything, for she wasn't in control, she was burning up. She was empty, aching deep, and throbbing with such intensity that she began to tremble.

Then he, too, was shocked, for he saw and felt her tremble and respond, and he was utterly still for one pounding moment. Then he was over her, pushing her back against the grass-cushioned ground, his mouth raking over her chin, down her throat, across the path his hand was making as he unbuttoned her blouse. She wore no bra, and his mouth was an abrupt jolt to her as he found one slight breast and suckled. She said something, or tried to, but it didn't sound at all coherent, and then she was ripping his shirt from his waistline and running her hands greedily underneath, and he surged against her.

From seemingly nowhere they fell into this sudden urgency, which stunned Devan's mind with incredulity. He was jerking off his shirt, and she was struggling to reach the zipper of his jeans, and then he was pulling her clothes off and coming to lie on top of her. Startling nudity, part of her was registering; startling and so exciting. She heard his voice, sounding low, utterly unlike himself, that measured Ryan she she had come to know, 'Did he get you this way? Did you tremble for him? Did he——'.

A moment of immobility, and then she thrust her hand into his hair and jerked his mouth roughly down to her. She hissed against his lips, 'Shut up.' And then she began to move.

And of course then it was all lost, for he was out of control and rough, and she was out of control and uncaring. Somehow, there in the cool breezes and on the bumpy ground, they were able to take pleasure from each other, both of them acting as though they were starved, and now drowning in assuagement of their need.

They lay very still, her head pressed against his shoulder, feeling his bare and silken skin as though for the first time, and his warmth. An eternity of exhausted immobility, his full weight on her, his face buried in her hair. Devan hid her face in Ryan's shoulder, breathing raggedly, feeling herself close to tears. Then she felt and heard him sigh. It brought her hands to the back of his neck to stroke lightly in the aftermath of her contentment.

Without moving, Ryan said very softly, 'This is damned uncomfortable.' It sent her to laughing into him instead of crying, which she considered was well enough. Then she bit him gently. He turned his head to her, and then caressed the side of her face with one hand. 'Are you all right?'

Devan hesitated, and then didn't bother to lie. 'I don't know.'

He pulled away from her slowly, and sat up. Without his body heat, cool air brushed against her overheated, damp skin, and she shivered. She let her eyes run over him, splendidly naked, and then he drew his shirt over her. But at that she sat up also, and looked about her rather tiredly for her scattered clothes. The grass was beginning to itch at her unprotected thighs.

'I hope you're not sorry,' he said, quietly, as he watched her.

She said on a half sob, 'I don't know what, or who I am.' His response was immediate as he came up on his knees and drew her into a tight, breath-crushing hug. Her head went down on his chest, sliding on still damp skin and hair. 'I—guess I'd better get dressed.'

His head bent as he nuzzled his face into her hair and he said gently, 'No need. Just draw on my shirt.'

'But Helen and the kids——'

'The kids were put to bed ages ago, and before I came out to find you, Helen had come to the kitchen to wish me good night. She's most likely asleep by now.'

He helped her draw on his shirt, and then buttoned it for her, with a long pressed kiss to her chest as he drew the material over her breasts. Then she slipped on her underwear, and he pulled on his jeans and shoes. When she had gathered her other things together, they turned in silence to walk back to the house, his arm tight and heavy across her shoulders.

The downstairs was indeed deserted and dark. Ryan locked the back door behind them and then

caught up with her at the bottom of the stairs.
Devan's head was bowed over shoulders which
looked slimmer than ever in his too-large shirt,
rolled up at the sleeves. When he reached her, he
tucked one arm under her knees, the other
wrapped around those slim shoulders, and he
picked her up. Her free arm crept around his neck
while her other held her clothes close to her chest.
He started to climb the steps. 'I do know how to
walk,' she informed his ear, in a whisper. At the
edge of her vision, she caught the glimmer of a
hard grin.

'Very good,' he congratulated, as quietly. 'Glad
to hear of it.' He went down the hall to her room.
'But all the same, I think I'll make sure you get
there.' He plonked her down without ceremony,
and then lay down over her, trying to read her
expression from the faint light coming from the
hall. She let herself look over him in response,
those features which were so hard, yet expressive.
His face became closed, wary. She lost all
consciousness of his naked chest at that look, her
eyes sharpening, body tensing. 'May I sleep with
you?'

Her mouth and face trembled, and then she
raised her arms to wrap them around his neck.
'What do you think?' she asked. After a moment,
he drew away to shut her bedroom door, and then
he stripped and climbed into her bed. After he had
pulled the covers over them both, she drew close
and fell asleep with his arms wrapped tightly
around her.

The next morning, when Devan awoke, Ryan was gone. She stretched, feeling the soreness in her muscles that she hadn't felt in a long time. A good feeling, that; an aching, tired, contented feeling. She sprawled from one corner of the bed to the other, lazily thinking about getting up. Vague and dreamlike memories brought a flush to her face and a smile to her lips. They had been so conscious of each other's presence. Whenever one had rolled over, the other would wake up and roll over too, so that their bodies were always curled close. They'd finally settled with him behind her, curling his longer body to hers, his arm heavy on her waist, his hand cupping her breast.

As she woke fully, however, the memories became overshadowed with her unresolved problems, and gradually she lost all pleasure in the thought of last night. She rolled over to her stomach and buried her head in one of her pillows, smelling his scent. Without meaning to, she had as much as told him she would be eager for a continuance of their relationship—in everything she'd done, in her urgent hands, in her enthusiastic, responsive lovemaking. He would expect too much from her, like Lee, and would be disappointed. It had been a colossal mistake. They'd gone too fast, too far, without communicating to each other their expectations.

She tensed. Expectations. He had a life and ties in New York. He had simply taken two weeks off, and she had been worried that he might want a long-term relationship. Of course he didn't; she was the one who did. Cold sweat broke over Devan's body. She wanted a relationship with him; she wanted to know and understand him; she wanted it as a continuance in her life; she wanted him. Last night hadn't been an isolated incident as far as she was concerned. She didn't have sexual relations with a man in a passing friendship. This was the second man she had gone to bed with, the first being Lee, when she had made commitments and had given faith. Lee had left her cold, had gone just like that, and she had been devastated, for she was a creature of intense emotions, and convictions, and desires. She gave too much of herself.

Devan whirled round and sat up with a thrust from the pillow, covering her face with her hands. She had been telling herself that she was a failure at her relationship with Lee all this time because she had believed him when he had said she hadn't tried hard enough. But could that be true, when she had given all her hope and dreams and emotion to it? She'd given so much of herself, she'd been left badly wounded, and barren.

Why had he left her? Why? *Why?*

'It's about time you woke up,' said Ryan from the open doorway, and her head snapped up to stare at him. 'Helen and the kids went grocery shopping.' He was leaning against the doorpost, and his eyes grew hard at what he saw in her expression. Then the look was gone as if it had never been. 'Any regrets?' he asked softly, watching her.

'Oh, Ryan,' she said on a shaky sigh, closing her

eyes. Then she opened them again, with her hand reaching out. She had meant to say something to him about her need for support, encouragement, but when she looked to the doorway, he wasn't there.

She tore out of the bed, rushed to the bathroom and quickly showered, then dressed. She skipped down the stairs quickly, and hurried to the kitchen. Ryan was standing at the screen door looking out while sipping from a cup. His face was hard, his mouth a thin line. She slowed down, trying to gauge his mood, and he threw over his shoulder expressionlessly, 'Help yourself to the coffee. I think you're ready for it by now.'

He was hurt. She realised that intuitively, for it certainly didn't show in his expression or in the nonchalance of his leaning body. He had misunderstood her and was hurt. A flashing, frightening thought. Did he regret last night? But she couldn't believe that.

She said quietly, 'You left before I could tell you how I missed you when I woke up.' A slow turn had him staring at her, head angled. That cold, repelling look faded, leaving him looking ruefully thoughtful at the vulnerable, tentative look in her eyes. She turned away and made for the coffee maker jerkily, dragging down a cup and pouring herself some. There was too much to understand about this complex man. She sighed, heavily, and whispered, 'I'm scared half to death of you.'

He went to the table to put down his cup. Then he walked behind her and gently tucked the hair

away from her cheek so that he could bend his head
and press a kiss by her mouth. At the feel of his
lips, her own shook. He said, gently, 'I rather think
I'm a little scared of you, too.'

'Well,' she said, as she leaned back to him for a
brief moment, 'that makes me feel a bit better.'

He went back to his coffee cup. Devan sipped at
her drink, the familiar brew tasting good to her,
and then she started to wander away aimlessly
when he looked at her sternly. 'Breakfast,' he
ordered, aggressively.

She looked and felt startled, and then laughed.
'All right!' She changed directions, back to the
worktop again and the refrigerator, and she said,
offhand, 'Besides, I'm ravenous.' That surprised
him into a laugh of his own.

She felt too lazy to cook, so she buttered bread
and ate three slices, along with one of the last fresh
oranges, and a second cup of coffee. Ryan had
wandered out of the room, so she lounged by
herself, a nice, relaxed feeling, considering how
intense the last few days had been. Paris was
outside, yowling forlornly, so she let him in and fed
him, listening to his contented purring as he
ravished the cat food in his dish.

The day was warm and bright, with fluffy clouds
scuttling past the sun and dimming the direct glow
from time to time. But there were never enough
clouds to make it a truly grey day, instead being
intensely yellow, blue and white. Devan rum-
maged for a book she had been meaning to read for
some time now but had never got around to, and

then she went out to the picnic table to bask in the shade of the overhanging tree and the warmth of the summer day. She was tired from their lovemaking last night and the series of emotions she'd run through in the last few days, so she soon found herself merely pretending to read. Then she wasn't even pretending, as she closed the book and lay along the length of the bench, her hair spilling off the seat, her legs hanging off the other end.

The screen door banged, and she lazily turned to watch under the table as Ryan strolled over. The morning had somehow slipped closer to noon while she'd lain there, and he was carefully carrying paper plates laden with sandwiches. Without a word he set one close to her, and then settled on the other bench to leisurely eat his lunch. She let her eyes roam over what she could see of him; his waist, his faded, casual jeans which hugged tight over hips and thighs, and those bare feet crossed at the ankles. A lazy sexual awareness pierced her, and it was a pleasant feeling to give in to.

She put her hand to the table without sitting up, and groped for her plate, which made him laugh quietly. Then she found the edge, and next sank her forefinger into bread, so she picked up her sandwich to nibble at it half-heartedly. 'When did Helen say she'd be back?'

'She wasn't sure. They had to buy shoes, so she said it might take some time. You know,' he went on to say, mildly, 'when I first got here, I couldn't believe that you'd willingly bury yourself here. I think I'm beginning to understand, now.'

Devan yawned, half covering her mouth with the hand that still held her sandwich. 'I'll have to admit that I didn't come here with a healthy aspect. But, as you've found, it does grow on you.' Birds chittered. A light wind rustled at the tree tops. Everything was lazy, on that day.

She reached out with her right hand and traced a light pattern on his denim-covered knee. His hand came under the table to grasp at her, but she'd seen him coming, and eluded him. 'What do you like to do, besides argue and get your own way?' she asked, and yawned again.

He laughed and retorted, 'What else is there?' She grinned, but kept silent, and after a moment he said carelessly, 'Oh, I guess I lead a pretty quiet social life. I go to almost all the Broadway plays, and I attend rather a lot of parties, most of which are through contacts I have in the business. But my work really takes up a lot of my time. I don't indulge in time-consuming hobbies.'

'You're very fit,' she commented, and traced his knee again with her fingernail, making his leg flex and his hand reach blindly for her.

'Cut that out, it tickles,' he said mildly. 'I play racquet ball in my lunch hour. What about you?'

'I like to tickle men,' she told him, and sent her hand to the underside of his thigh, scratching maddeningly. This time he caught her hand in a very firm grip, and bent to peer under the table at her laughing eyes. He smiled slowly and then he yanked her right off the bench. She fell to the ground with an audible thud and lost the rest of her sandwich. Then she was giggling hilariously as, still with a tight hold on her wrist, he started to drag her to him, an unspoken, unknown intent in his smiling, light eyes.

She was tangled between his legs when he finally stopped hauling on her, and she was able to get her knees underneath her. But he hadn't let go and he wrapped his free arm tightly around her waist. For a moment she thought he meant to kiss her and went breathless, but then his fingers found their way between shirt and jeans and he was suddenly, ruthlessly, inexorably tickling her ribs. She gave a strangled scream and her body convulsed. But his hold was too firm, and finally she was crying from laughing so hard and jerking about in a frantic effort to get loose, trapped between his legs with the picnic table at her back.

'Stop, please!' she gasped, jerking as far back as she could, and bumping the back of her head on the edge of the table. She saw stars, and he did stop then, immediately, laughing as hard as she, as her hand went to ruefully cup the back of her head.

'I'm sorry,' he told her, remorsefully chuckling as he, too, felt at the back of her head. Cool, hardy fingers under her hair, and she instantly forgave him. 'I thought I had a tight enough grip on you.'

Devan regained control of herself and looked at him with her eyes still laughing, a little wild. Then she sank her teeth into his upper arm, growling. She was careful not to hurt him and he indulgently looked down as she did it, but then his body was jerking as, with her jaws moving delicately back and forth, she tickled him with her teeth. He sank his hand into her hair and pulled her back. She laughed up to his bent face, loving every minute of it.

As she watched, the amusement slowly died out of his bright eyes, leaving them smoky, darkening. Then they shuttered, and he pulled her up to take her lips in a long, searching, deep-drinking kiss. She shifted close to him, feeling his thighs tight against her, her breasts pressed against his hard chest as he hunched to reach her mouth.

He pulled back and, as he stared down at her, he growled, 'I'm glad he was a fool. I'm glad he left you.'

Once again, he had brought Lee into the situation when the last thing she wanted was to be reminded of the past. As he came back down, his intention quite clear, she jerked her head away. He held stiff for a moment, and then he relaxed with a sigh, putting his face to the top of her fragrant hair.

'Mistake?' he asked.

She put her forehead to his arm as he loosely cradled her. 'Big one.' His hand stroked the back of her head, and she rubbed her cheek against the material of his shirt. 'We have to talk about last night.'

'We have to talk about a hell of a lot of other things, too,' he said, rather grimly. Then, more softly, 'Look, I'm sorry I keep dragging him up.'

'Then why do you do it?' she snapped.

She felt the muscles in his arm bunch spasmodically. He said from the back of his throat, 'Because he's still a part of your life, and I don't want him to be.' She froze, shocked. Then Ryan was dragging her head back so that he could stare down at her face. The sun had come out from behind a cloud, and she was dazzled by the glare falling through tree branches, lighting the edges of his hair to pale yellow. 'Because I'm finding that I resent that he had your body at all.'

She drew back out of his arms. He let her go and strode several paces away, rubbing at the back of his neck, his back to her. She sank weakly to the bench. 'What has got into you?' she demanded, upset. 'You sound like you *own* me or something. For God's sake, I'm free to sleep with whomever I like, with no judgment from you——'

'I'm not judging you!' he half shouted, whirling about to stare at her with brilliant eyes. 'I am *not* judging you! If that had been my morality, I never would have made love with you last night.'

'Then what is it?' There were implications in what he was saying, she just didn't know how to read them, unsure of herself and frustrated with it.

'It's not logical, that's what it is!' he snapped, thrusting his hand through his hair. He stood with his weight on one hip, his hand resting on it, and he looked baffled, disgusted with himself.

Her expression turned wry. She could well understand how he would feel frustration. He was a logical, clear-thinking man. He had to be, in his profession, discerning and shrewd. He couldn't be liking this at all. 'Surely,' she said, much quieter, more reasonable, 'surely you've been with other women?'

His glance at her was dry. 'What do you think?'

She looked away at random. 'I think that it appears we have a double standard, here. Men can have sex, women can't. Who, then, do the men have sex with?'

He exploded, 'That isn't how I feel!'

She retorted, her words swift on the heel of his, 'I think that's precisely how you feel. It's just not how you think. The two are not the same.'

He said as though it were jerked out of him, 'Damn you, don't tell me how I think or feel!'

Her eyes widened on him, and then blazed molten hot. 'Right,' she said, with an audible snap of her teeth. She rocketed off the bench and strode for the house. She never made it. She froze halfway there, putting her foot gently down as she stopped, realisation stunning her rather late. Then she pivoted to stare at Ryan who was grimly watching her leave. His face was brooding, his eyes bleakly grey under frowning brows. She searched his expression, and then slowly, delightedly, grinned. 'You're jealous,' she said, as if in accusation.

'I got to hand it to you, Devan,' he snapped sarcastically, his hands on his hips. 'You are really bright.'

He hadn't meant it to be funny but she laughed anyway, her anger evaporating in the summer breeze. He reacted as if whipped, fury darkening in his eyes, and he strode over to yank her into his arms. She met his fierce kiss and matched him, draping her arms around his neck while the fingers of both his hands dug into her waist, making marks. She concentrated on the feel of his mouth, open and hard and still angry, moving wet, while her fingers lightly drew through his silken hair, shaping the back of his head.

Then her heart began to pound as he took her and deliberately knocked her off balance. She stumbled, her weight going sideways, clinging to him. But he wasn't stationary. He was moving, too, lowering her to the ground and coming with her, his long legs heavy and tangled with hers as he drove in as deep as either of them could bear with his tongue. His hand came up to mould her breast, and she arched against him, making him groan.

He dragged his head back and stared down at her blindly. Then he looked around and gave an odd little laugh. 'What if your sister drove up? Let's go inside.'

She was losing herself in him, and it was a measure of how far gone she really was that she didn't care. She just looked at him, her body reawakened and eager, and she whispered, 'OK.'

There was exultation at the back of his eyes. He drew away from her and pulled himself to a squatting position as she tremblingly sat, then stood. She turned to him and something white caught her attention. When she looked, she saw one of their paper plates tumbling over and over on the ground, blown by the wind. She sighed, feeling the sexual tension ease somewhat, and then without a word Ryan went to pick up the wandering plate while she went to the picnic bench to pick up the other, along with her dropped, dirty sandwich and her book.

She had one knee propped on the bench while she reached for the two things on the table, setting the inedible food on the plate, and for a moment she just leaned on her two hands and hung her head. She quickly and intensely wished she hadn't seen that white flutter, wished that Ryan had chosen to either press their lovemaking outside, regardless of the risk of exposure, or had carried her indoors like he'd carried her last night. But he hadn't and her physical fervour had cooled, leaving her with doubts, with fears, with the realisation that theirs was a transient relationship. She suddenly couldn't afford to give any more of herself to what she felt for Ryan.

She picked up the things and turned back towards the house, mentally squaring her shoulders. She dreaded what was to come, but couldn't see any other path to take. Ryan was, she saw, already inside and leaning against the doorway with his habitual nonchalance; as she approached the house, she searched his expression through the thin wire mesh. He pushed the screen open for her, and she came inside, tossing the sandwich and the paper plate with a careless flick of the wrist. She looked to the floor, feeling awkward, and said heavily, 'I've—changed my mind.'

CHAPTER NINE

WHAT brought Devan's head snapping up was Ryan's expressionless, 'I know.' When she stared at him, all she saw was remoteness. Tightly remote, with nothing of the frustration and puzzlement she had expected, nothing but that repelling façade.

She said, as if goaded, 'I'm not playing a game with you. I'm sorry.'

He shrugged uncaringly, and without a word walked out of the house. She stood as though she were the one let down, and when she heard his car start to quiet life, followed quickly by the crunch of gravel as he backed out of the driveway, her face crumpled into unexplainable tears. She bent her head and put a hand over her eyes.

She was looking quite normal and composed when Helen and the children came home, and the house was filled again with cheerfulness. But the afternoon drifted by, agonisingly slow for her. She busied herself with cleaning the first floor bathroom, an unthinking job. Her ears were tuned to any noise from the front garden, and she knew that what she was really doing was killing time while she waited for Ryan to come back. Then she went to her room and slowly made her bed, though she considered it now to be something of a waste of time since it would be occupied again before long. Occupied by whom?

She balled her hands into tight fists, gripping the blankets in a bone-white clench. She didn't want to sleep alone, God help her. But, after this afternoon, she seriously doubted that Ryan would consider staying with her. That was supposed to be for the best. Why couldn't she feel that?

As the afternoon slipped to early evening, she went downstairs and listlessly began to help Helen prepare supper. She found herself getting agitated, uptight, hot and worried. Why wasn't he returning? He had left, just like that; no warning, just like—Lee.

She sank into a chair slowly, while Helen, humming, worked over the stove. Devan's expression was calm, her eyes desperate. He wouldn't, he couldn't, just leave. He had things in the house. Didn't he? He knew what Lee had done to her and, while their relationship was not quite as involved, while the situation was not quite the same, he wouldn't be so terrible as to just leave.

She leaped to her feet and raced through the house, unaware that Helen had turned to stare at her in puzzlement. Something, there had to be something of his in the house—he hadn't even been wearing his shoes—there. She slowed, then stopped, and very nearly began to cry again as she saw his suitcase, tucked tidily into a corner of the guest bedroom. Tidily, as Ryan did everything, put away from sight, and his shoes were tucked beside it.

She was behaving stupidly and she knew it. Then anger stormed through her. He hadn't worn his damned shoes, was actually driving barefoot. The idiotic man! Devan realised how disproportionate and silly her anger was over something so utterly trivial, and she sagged weakly against the end of his bed in reaction. Why the hell should she care if he possibly got a ticket? Chances were that nothing would come of it, providing he wasn't in an accident. She tensed again. An accident. It was possible; he had been gone so long. She balled her hands into fists and put them over her eyes. What was wrong with her? Why was she acting so ridiculously?

The unmistakable sounds of someone's arrival had her stumbling off the bed and dashing for her bedroom window. She looked outside and saw Ryan uncurling from the driver's seat of his car, his hair tangled from the wind, his expression no less remote than it had been when he had left. He somehow managed to escape looking comical without his shoes. She suddenly didn't want him catching her hanging out of her window, so she hurried for the kitchen, taking the stairs two at a time, and feverishly dragged dishes and cutlery from the cupboard to set the table. This time she saw Helen's blank stare, and knew she was acting quite oddly, but ignored the look anyway.

The screen door banged as he silently walked in just the same way he had left, and she stopped in the middle of the floor, her hands full of plates and cutlery, her eyes full of uncertainty. He glanced at her once and then away, and he cut through the kitchen as though heading for another room.

'Hi,' said Helen cheerfully.

Ryan looked at her older sister, and his face softened into a smile. Devan suddenly wanted to slap the pair of them. 'Hi, yourself,' he said. 'When's supper?'

'In about half an hour, I should think,' said Helen, looking around at the mess she was making. 'By the way, I want to thank you again for helping with the grocery bill. It wasn't at all necessary, I assure you——'

'Nonsense,' he said warmly. 'I was an uninvited guest. The least I could do was to pay for my food.'

He walked away. Suddenly Devan was desperate to keep him from leaving, and she bolted for the dining room. 'Ryan——' she started, catching him as he was just starting up the stairs. He stopped dead. She realised she was still holding the dishes, and she looked at them a little blankly. Then she walked over to the dining table and set them all down carefully. She took the forks and lined them up, and then took the spoons and did the same with them. He slowly walked back to her. 'This morning,' she said, her low voice coming a little strangled, 'I realised that Lee had to have been wrong about something, at least, in what he told me. I gave far more to the relationship than he gave me credit for.' She was busy looking at the knives she was lining up, so she didn't see Ryan silently tense as he stared at her, as if he expected to be struck. She whispered, 'I'm afraid of giving that much of myself again, and being hurt.'

Long, long seconds ticking by. She shifted the forks, and put them in alternate positions with the spoons. 'I—see,' said Ryan from behind her finally, and her fingers jerked, sending the cutlery scattering. Then he said stiltedly, 'You're referring to this afternoon, I take it.'

'I'm sorry,' she whispered, dismally. She didn't know what she meant when she said it.

He then asked her, with an obvious note of caution in his voice and in his choice of words, 'You feel that you're in danger of getting too deeply involved with me?'

She bit at her lips and trembled. She couldn't give a verbal reply, couldn't even move; for she felt as if she was pinned and exposed under a bright harsh light, naked to the open air and pitiless eyes.

He walked over to her and stopped just at her side. After a moment he let one of his hands rest heavily on her shoulder, and he sucked in his breath when he felt how she shook. 'Devan,' he said, sounding not at all like himself. 'I'm going back to New York at the end of the week, instead of staying the second.' She couldn't have expected anything different, and she closed her eyes in desolation. But then he was whispering, 'Would you come back with me?'

She stopped breathing, unable to believe that she had heard him right. Then her head jerked up and she was staring at him with huge, dilated eyes, dark in a white face. He looked very rigid, his expression held very sternly, his mouth compressed into a hard, white line. She opened and closed her own mouth like an idiot, and then managed to stammer, 'Wha—what did you say?' Anger ran swiftly over his face, and she blurted out, 'Just—let me hear it, all right?'

'I want you to come back with me,' he said tonelessly, his hand falling away from her shoulder. She looked at the table and the scattered cutlery, and automatically reached for the spoons. 'Why?' she asked, feeling stupid with the confusion teeming in her. He made an impatient movement. 'I mean, what would you be expecting from me? What can I hope to get from you? Ryan, I—I'm not sure I want to live in New York again.'

He walked over to the wall and looked over a framed picture with great concentration. 'I don't want anything from you that you aren't prepared to give. I want you to come and stay with me at my apartment. On a trial basis, if you'd like. No strings, nor commitments. I'd like us to have the chance to get to know each other better, in an everyday, long-term setting.'

His shoulders were held square, and she walked almost reluctantly over to him to place her hand between his shoulder blades. She could feel the muscles bunched into rock hardness, and she absently began to smooth at them with her fingers. Underneath the shock of his unexpected offer, a secret, deep-lying exultation began to swell. She dampened it down severely. 'I don't know what to say,' she whispered, and his head went back as he stared at the ceiling.

'Just say yes or no.' His voice was in stern control, almost indifferent.

She felt hot with a sudden panic. 'Right now? Can't I think about it, just a little bit?'

He then turned to look at her, and his voice grew gentle as he said, 'That's why I'm staying until the end of the week.'

Helen said brightly from the doorway of the kitchen, 'What a good idea!' Both Ryan and Devan swivelled to stare at her blankly. Helen looked up from staring at the dining room table. 'I think we should have started eating in here when Ryan arrived. There's much more room on this table.'

The tense, awkward moment was broken. Devan turned her gaze to the table then, too, and she had to shake her head and laugh at the crazy pattern of cutlery. She went to flick on the dining room light, and set the table right.

They sat down to eat, and supper passed by easily enough. If Devan was a bit pale and preoccupied, nobody, except perhaps Ryan, really noticed, what with the children's chatter, and Ryan keeping the conversational ball rolling with Helen. Afterwards Devan refused all help in cleaning up, and shooed everyone into the living room before stacking the dishes and carrying them into the kitchen.

When she was finished, she wandered towards the front of the house and leaned against the back

of the armchair Helen was curled up in. At her feet,
Janie and Gary were playing a game. Ryan was
comfortably installed on the couch, his feet
propped up on one arm. He turned his head and
met her eyes for a long, wordless moment.

'Helen,' he then said casually, 'I'd better let you
know. I've decided not to stay the second week.'

Her sister was obviously surprised, and a little
distressed. 'Really? Good heavens, what a shame!
I was so looking forward to it. Are you sure you
won't change your mind?'

'Quite sure,' he said quietly, his gaze holding
Devan's. Janie and Gary totally ignored them.
Helen, noting the direction of his gaze, slowly
turned her head to look thoughtfully at Devan,
also. 'I think,' he continued, 'that you deserve to
understand the situation, as you've been so patient
and hospitable these last few days. I've asked
Devan to come back with me.'

That caught the children's attention. Helen
looked back at Ryan, her head swivelling like an
owl's, and there was a long moment of digestive
silence. 'For good?' she asked, quite carefully.
'And what did Devan say?'

'Damn it, don't talk about me as though I'm not
here,' she said, irritably. Her sister turned back
round, her questioning gaze full on her, and Devan
snapped, 'I haven't given him an answer, yet.'

Then Janie spoke up, her freckles standing out
against her pale skin, 'Aunt Devan, you can't go
back to New York. You said you'd live with us!'

She closed her eyes for a moment at the pain in

her niece's voice. Then she said, as gently as possible, 'But I never said I'd live here for ever. Besides, I haven't made up my mind yet.'

'Just tell him no!' Janie's eyes shone, overbright. Even Gary, who was generally imperturbable, looked somewhat stricken. Devan had to put her face down in her hand as she leaned against the chair, her heart welling with a strange emotion, close to grief. She had honestly not expected this kind of response.

She whispered, 'I can't do that, sweetheart.' She thought she heard Ryan sigh.

Janie looked down at the cards she was holding, and she threw them to the floor. 'I don't want to play any more,' she said, muffled, and she scrambled to her feet to run upstairs. Gary, his game ruined, turned to glare at Ryan as though it were all his fault. Devan pushed herself away from the armchair, intending to go upstairs to talk with Janie, but Helen forestalled her.

'Let me do it,' her sister said softly.

'I didn't know she would take it this way,' she said wretchedly.

'I know. It'll be all right. She's just had a shock, that's all,' said Helen soothingly. She had just enough time to notice that her sister didn't look at all surprised, and she wondered at that. 'Just let me talk to her tonight.'

'OK.'

'Come on, Gary,' Helen said then. 'Let's go. It's bathtime, anyway.' To everyone's surprise, he didn't even argue; he just shuffled his cards together, climbed to his feet, and stumped up the stairs behind his mother, with his head down.

As soon as they were gone, Devan rounded on a very thoughtful-looking Ryan who was sitting up now, his elbows resting on his knees, instead of sprawling at his ease. 'Why the hell did you have to say anything?'

He stared at the carpet in front of him, and his mouth twisted. 'Because they deserve to know what is going on between you and me. And if, by any chance, you should decide to come back with me, it would be extremely unfair of you to just up and leave one day.' She whitened as if he'd struck her, and he said gently, 'I have it on good authority that they would feel betrayed.'

She said through stiff lips, 'You're right. I'm sorry for snapping at you.'

One side of his twisted mouth rose lopsidedly in an unamused smile. 'I don't suppose you've had time to make up your mind, have you?' She made her way around the side of the chair and sat down heavily as she shook her head. 'No, I didn't think so.' He regarded her as she stared glumly ahead of her with unfocused eyes. Then he asked, 'Might I ask you a question, and then I'll never bring it up again?'

That brought her eyes into focus and she stared at him sharply before sighing. 'About Lee.'

His face closed. 'Yes.'

She searched those light grey-blue eyes, now becoming so familiar to her, and then she said shortly, 'All right. Just this once. Then the subject's closed?'

'I swear.' He just stared back frowningly, in silence, as though he dreaded to ask the question, and she unconsciously began to tense. 'What would happen if you were to see him again, say at a theatre, or at a party? How would you feel if you were to find out where he was?'

She rubbed at her nose with thumb and forefinger, and pointed out, 'That's two questions.' He shifted impatiently, and she relented. 'All right. I don't know to the first question. I would hope that I would treat the situation with some grace, but I probably would end up ignoring him. As far as the second goes, I've always known how to get in touch with him. Hell, he works at the paper I used to. If it were a matter of me getting in contact with him, I could do it in a minute, with just a phone call. But he was the one who left me. If he didn't want to come back or get in touch, I didn't have anything to say to him.'

He looked incredulous, his eyes full of something shocked and dark. 'You —knew where he was the whole time? He worked where you worked?'

'That's how we met,' she said simply, staring at him.

'What does he do?'

'Last I knew, he wrote political commentaries. I suppose he might have had a promotion since then. He might even be an editor by now.' She stirred in her chair.

After a moment, Ryan asked oddly, 'Was he any good?'

She had to think about that, a little nonplussed. Then she shrugged. 'Yeah, sure. His style was always quite a bit different from mine, and of course we were involved in different subjects, but he was certainly good at what he did. He was quite intelligent.' She regarded him with a little suspicion. 'What are you thinking?'

He laced and unlaced his fingers, watching them. They were long on large hands, the nails well kept. 'Do you remember when I asked you if you were afraid of your own success?'

'Of course. It was a stupid thing to say.'

He said impatiently, 'Forget that a minute. I was just wondering—what if, perhaps, *Lee* was afraid of your success?'

'What do you mean—that he was jealous?' she asked, incredulously. 'But how could he be. Our writing was so different. No, I don't buy that.'

It was his turn to shrug. 'It was just a thought.' Then he stood. 'I think I'm going to turn in now. I haven't had a whole lot of sleep in the last few days.' That was said with some wryness.

'Oh, but——' she started, making a gesture towards him as he began to stride by her. He stopped immediately, looking down at her enquiringly, his head angled, his eyes patient, his expression somewhat wary. She felt another welling of that panic from earlier; time was trickling by so quickly, and soon he would be heading back to New York, with or without her.

She dropped her eyes and whispered, 'It's nothing. Good night.'

He drew close and bent over her, pressing his lips to her forehead. She couldn't think why it made her want to cry. 'Good night.'

Left by herself, she brooded in the silence. Her mind kept whirling back to what Ryan had suggested about Lee. Dear heaven, could that have really been what happened? But no, he would have been far more rational about it; he had been a rational man. Wouldn't he?

She thought of his cautions and admonitions when she had started her first novel. She had discounted it then as part of his cautious nature, but had it been more? Suddenly memories tumbled over themselves in her mind. His resentment from time to time when she would work in the evening instead of going out with him. The cooling of physical relations just before he had left. The reticence he had shown in the face of her popular, and therefore monetary, success. For the first time, and in spite of her initial protest, everything began to make sense.

She had felt rage, hurt and betrayal when Lee had left her, and echoes of those emotions had dogged her footsteps for a year now. For the first time she began to feel a sneaking sense of compassion for him. He had allowed his insecurities to cripple what he had once felt for her when, at the very basest level, her writing hadn't mattered in the slightest. She remembered Ryan telling her that with a bit of a jolt, and then she ruefully smiled. He had indeed been right, and perhaps that was what made her stories work. There were some things she would always hold to be more important than her writing, it was just that in the last year her perspective had become a bit tangled. Lee had been more important; Helen and the children were far more important; Ryan was now more important. All these things in the background had given her the impetus to write.

Insecurity. She hoped Lee was managing to be happy, but she rather feared that he would always be disappointed in himself for leaving her, and ashamed of how he had tried to justify it, whereas now that she had finally managed to work past her anger, she could put him behind her and go on with her life.

And who was she to judge? Wasn't insecurity tying her up right at this very moment, making her waver in indecision, making her wonder at the depth of Ryan's feelings for her? As far as that went, Ryan battled with insecurity also, and it had showed in his angrily declared jealousy of her preoccupation with her past love affair. She felt suddenly sad at the unnecessary pain they all went through, even down to Janie's surprisingly deep pain at the thought of her departure.

Tomorrow, she thought, I'll have to make sure I tell her how much I love her. And then she turned her head at the sound of light approaching footsteps. Helen came round the armchair to sit rather tiredly on the couch. She looked at Devan and said, as though reading her mind, 'Janie's afraid that you don't love us any more.'

'Oh, no!' Devan groaned. 'I'll talk to her tomorrow.'

Helen said carefully, 'I don't know him very well, but I think Ryan is a good man. Have——'

'I decided? No. I don't know what to do.' She bowed her head and sighed.

'I just came down to ask,' said her sister, who rose and then came to the armchair and knelt in front of her. 'It's pretty simple if you can manage it, Devan. Just be happy.' With a quick, tight hug, Helen whisked through the downstairs, turning off lights and closing windows and doors. She left the upstairs hall light on as she always did, and then she disappeared quickly into her room.

Devan sat for some time in the small pool of light shining from the single living room lamp. She was alone in her indecision, and somehow she had never felt quite so lonely before. She dreaded going upstairs to her empty bed. She longed for warm skin and low murmurs. She longed for Ryan, and last night had only intensified the longing.

She lifted her head, feeling the light sheen of sweat on her forehead and upper lip. It was hot tonight. She breathed as though labouring under some kind of physical stress. She was suddenly utterly wearly, and she dragged herself out of the chair to turn out the light and ascend the stairs slowly, counting each one. The upstairs hall, the lit corridor. The closed doors sheltering each one in his own darkness, except for Gary's, for he hated the dark. She paused by Ryan's door, swallowed hard and felt herself tremble.

And quickly passed by, to splash cold water on her face and brush her teeth madly. But back in the hall again, on her way to her room, his door drew her. She slowly put her hand on the doorknob, slowly turned it, hearing the tiny snick as it unlatched. Then she pushed the door silently open. Her heart was pounding. She knew that just one sound from him, one discouraging noise, and she would bolt for her room. The light from the partially opened door fell over his bare chest, turning silver shadow to human skin. He murmured, and turned his head away from the light, and then froze. Slowly his head came back round, his light eyes staring at her, sparkling.

Suddenly everything settled into simplicity for her, and she whispered, as forthright as he had been, 'May I sleep with you, please?'

He smiled. It drew her like a magnet, that sleepy, open look, that singularly sweet smile stretching over his mature features. She carefully shut the door behind her and walked quietly over to the side of his bed.

He sat up, the sheet falling from his torso, and helped her to undress with warm fingers. She came under the covers and against his long limbs, suddenly chilled. His window was open and fresh air gusted gently in from time to time, along with the slight country noises.

'I hoped you would come,' he said, quietly.

She was trembling now from the feeling of his bare length against hers, and she turned to her side and propped herself up on one elbow. She ran her fingers lightly over his mouth. 'How could I resist?' she whispered. He pressed a kiss.

Then he stirred beside her, and one hand came up to tenderly stroke at hers, lying now on his chest. 'We have some unfinished business, I think.' She could hear the smile in his voice, along with something else, something languorous and exciting.

Her fingers were now tracing through the light sprinkles of hair on his rising and falling chest. 'I take it you are referring to this afternoon?' she murmured.

Shadowy gleam of white as he grinned, and he started to rise. She put gentle pressure on his chest to restrain him. 'No. I stopped it this afternoon,' she told him. 'It's only fair that I start it tonight.' She drew over him, and then hesitated, doubtfully. 'Do you mind?'

At that he laughed, low and incredulous. 'Why on earth would I mind?' His hands gently guided her atop him, and ran down her thighs in a caress. 'Lady, you have the strangest notions sometimes. What difference does it make who's on top?'

She leaned over him, her elbows on either side of his head, and as she took his lips she was laughing too, low and deep down, with great delight.

Much later, she lay sprawled exhaustedly against him and listened to his deep, steady breathing. She floated quite close to the edge of sleep, and knew a deep contentment from what she and Ryan had shared. Somehow his last coherent statement had made a deep impression on her, and she realised with some amazement that he had truly meant it. They shared equally in their passion, a give and take, a quiet expectation of responsibility on both sides.

She wondered sleepily if he knew what he was doing to her as she threaded slow, lethargic fingers through the hair at the back of his head. She had once thought she was barren, like an empty hearth, but he had started something glowing deep inside her. It burned steadily, a rose-coloured ember, and she was beginning to suspect that it might last beyond all else, beyond youth, ambition, stamina and physical desire, a warmth to last her through all the winters of her life.

CHAPTER TEN

AFTER the previous night's storm, the day was sunny and dewy wet, with sparkling green and yellow leaves and clean washed grass. Devan watched Ryan store everything in the car, and Helen stood beside her, the children close behind. Nobody said very much; there didn't seem to be anything left to say.

Then Ryan was walking back to the front porch where everything had started just a short time before. He stood and watched silently as Devan turned to Helen to give her a hard hug. 'I'll call you when we get there,' she promised in her sister's ear. Then she drew back and Helen tried to smile. 'This mightn't even be for that long. It's just a visit.'

At that Helen did manage a smile, though her eyes sparkled like the wet grass and leaves. 'We'll see.' When Devan turned to the children, Helen said a quiet goodbye to Ryan, who quickly hugged her tight, much to her pleased discomfiture.

Janie looked as though she might screw up her face and break into tears at any moment, and Gary scowled angrily from under his yellowish thatch of hair. 'Well,' said Devan, too brightly. 'Don't I get a hug from either of you?'

That brought Janie to her in a rush, and the girl

clasped her close before stepping back, her carrot head bowed. Then Gary hurtled to her and nearly sent her over backwards. He practically choked her to death; he even smacked a rough kiss in the vicinity of her nose. That he missed and hit her painfully in the eye, neither was in a state to mention. She stood back and looked at the pair, who stared alternately at the ground and the sky. Her heart welled at the solemn look on their rounded young faces. She searched for something to say to lighten the mood.

Suddenly she hit upon it; her eyes narrowed on the two dangerously. 'Wait a minute,' she said slowly. They looked at her, startled. Ryan, who had been rather quiet the last two days, even after last night when she had made up her mind to come with him for a short time, tensed. But Devan didn't see as she glowered at her niece and nephew, and then, with a wicked, wicked smile, said gently, 'I believe I owe you both something.'

Janie's eyes widened; Gary's eyes positively sparkled with delight. 'What do you mean?' asked her niece, doubtful of the look on her face, as well she should be.

'Do you remember once upon a time, when a beastly little savage scalped me, and a horrid brat then dumped water on my head?' reminded Devan sweetly, taking a step forward. The two looked at each other, and Gary's face grew as apprehensive as Janie's as they both edged a step backward. They did indeed. 'I believe I promised I'd get you back, didn't I?' she went on conversationally. 'Say your prayers, imps. Retribution has come.'

Whether they understood the meaning of that word or not was to be doubted, but they most certainly understood the meaning behind it, and, with another exchanged, disconcerted look, they decided to bolt. Janie crashed into the house and Gary followed close on her heels, while Devan was in hot pursuit. Helen just smiled and leaned against the porch rail to chat with an amused, patient Ryan while they waited.

Strange sounds came from the interior of the house, bumps and shrieks and roars. Something fell over with a resounding crash that the two on the porch could have sworn made the house shake. After a good ten minutes, Devan finally appeared at the front door, shakily. Her hair was wild, her eyes gleefully dancing. She was breathing heavily, and her blouse was twisted awry; she automatically straightened it as she exhaustedly pushed through the screen door.

She ran her fingers through her hair, utter silence coming from the house, and then said to Ryan composedly, 'Ready to go?' Her sister stared at her in horrified fascination, longing to ask what she had done to the children but not quite daring, while Ryan's shoulders shook in silent laughter.

'I am if you are,' he said.

She whispered to Helen, 'Rescue them in a little bit.' And with that cryptic message, they left.

She had managed to bring the children's mood

up, but couldn't suppress her own feelings any longer as they pulled away from the house that had been home to her for more than a year now. She looked behind her, a strange, yearning emotion threatening to choke her in the throat, and only after the house was well out of sight did she turn round to rummage in her bag for her brush. She straightened her gleaming hair savagely.

'By the way,' Ryan said, 'what did you do to them?'

'The children?' she asked. A wan smile touched her lips. 'I locked them in Gary's wardrobe. It is, I assure you, a fate worse than death!' He laughed.

The memory had brought her spirits up, but they soon plunged again. She couldn't think what was the matter with her. When she had decided to come with Ryan, she had made it very clear to him that it was to be considered an extended visit only, and that she would leave at any time she wished. His response had been mild, without argument. They hadn't even taken any of her heavier things, just clothes for the stay. But she felt as though she were leaving Helen and the children for ever, and her eyes stung at the thought.

An hour into the drive, across the state line, Devan knew she had made a terrible mistake. She didn't know this man, didn't even want to live in New York again, couldn't think why she was travelling south with him when all she wanted suddenly, intensely, was to be at home playing

Monopoly with Janie while Gary threw paper aeroplanes at their heads.

The morning was spent silently. They stopped for a break and cold drinks in Vermont, and then continued on their way. Ryan was brooding, she could tell, his expression slightly frowning, incommunicable, distant. She slouched in her seat, her safety belt loosened around her slim waist, and stared dreamily out of her open window at the countryside flashing by. Interstate highways, dark blue road, white and yellow painted lines. Green land, blue sky, white cloud. Shadowed, hot interior of the car, steady rhythm. Her head slid to one side, and she dozed.

And woke again to a different feel to the air, noise, traffic. Everywhere there were rushing people. They were coming to a heavily travelled area; she knew by looking around her that New York lay not far to the south-west. She sat up, feeling rumpled and stupid. Ryan looked much as he had about eighty miles back. It was the countryside that had changed. She drew out her brush again and used it on her hair, checking her handbag mirror briefly and then looking about her intently, feeling her senses quicken.

In a flash, it seemed that they were through the surrounding suburbs. And in a crash, it seemed that the city was upon her. Her eyes brightened and sparkled as she looked about her. Dirty and grey; gaudy and bright; old tumbled houses and

sleek gleaming skyscrapers; elegant people striding down the avenues; pathetic old ladies digging
out of dustbins; children everywhere; a musician
playing in the street for money and the love of
performing; a juggling man with a monkey sitting
on his shoulder and jabbering at passers by. Ultra-
luxurious limousines pulling to a stop behind
battered '65 Chevrolets; a group of students
dancing in the streets; a bearded black-clad rabbi
stepping delicately around three sprawling drunks.
New York.

The neighbourhood he drove through and then
slowed down in was about half an hour from where
she and Lee used to live. It gave her a strange
feeling as she looked around the unfamiliar streets
and apartment houses. Half an hour from this
man, and their paths had never crossed. Four
novels and a mutual lack of interest; professional,
remote; editor and author. They had both been
busy with their own separate lives and problems,
and now they were lovers. Panic, now familiar
from the last few days, gripped her in a sweating
hold. This should not be happening.

He pulled up to the kerb and stopped. 'I'm not
supposed to park here,' he told her with a crooked
smile, 'but I think we'll be safe enough until we get
the luggage inside. Then, while you nose around
my apartment, I'll get rid of the car. It should only
take me about half an hour. Do you mind?'

'Of course not,' she said quickly, and they
climbed out. He took most of the things, except for

the overnight bag of hers that she clutched along with her handbag. They ran up the wide concrete steps. She glanced quickly down the names listed by the door as he unlocked it, but didn't have time to see his before he was pushing open the door and stepping back for her to enter. 'Second floor,' he directed, as he bent again for the suitcases, and, with a glance around at the carpeted halls and steps, she started up the flight.

His apartment was spacious, but she hadn't expected anything else. The kitchen was small, tucked behind a waist-high counter with a dining table on the opposite side. The living room was large, with a white stone fireplace, and well decorated. Ryan deposited his load with a thump to the floor just inside the door, and he hesitated for a moment, looking at her somewhat oddly. He started to speak and then hesitated as she looked at him silently, enquiringly, distantly. Apparently he was feeling the sudden barrier between them as much as she. 'I'd better take care of the car,' he said finally. 'Will you be all right?'

'Yes, of course I will,' she said lightly, moving around the corner of his couch. 'I'll just look around, if you don't mind.'

'Be my guest.' At those words, for some reason, he looked fleetingly rueful, but he quickly smiled at her and then shut the door as he left. She heard the lock click at his departure, and grimaced. At Helen's she had got out of the habit of locking doors, but then again, this was New York.

She wandered through the rest of the apartment. A large, modern bathroom, two bedrooms, one used as such, of course, and the other converted into a library startlingly similar to hers. She felt an absurd surge of comfort at that, and then spent a great deal of time browsing through his extensive collection of books. When she found all of hers, in hardback, she had to close her eyes tight against an unsettling, choked emotion. He had her books, ones that she had written not so long ago, not so very far away, but in a totally different life. She had lived in her cramped apartment while he had lived here. She'd had different expectations then from her life. She had been younger, more intense, tough.

Her mood shifted unexpectedly, with a small laugh. She approached his antique wardrobe, which smelled of sandalwood, and she looked at herself in the full-length mirror. Come to think of it, she was still young, in the prime of her life, and as for the intensity of her moods, she only had to look at how she swung back and forth from one moment to the next, violently, to ascertain the strength of her emotions. Granted, she wasn't as tough as she used to be, but there was something rather appealing in the vulnerability in her eyes. She hoped.

Ryan's scent lingered in the bedroom, the faint spice of the aftershave he used. She could close her eyes and feel that he was about to wrap his arms around her from behind. His place of rest, his home, his bed. All of it was strange to her. The walls suddenly seemed to close in on her, and she rushed back to the larger living room, wishing nothing more than to get out of this place, to go back to Maine.

There were steps outside, and a key sounded in the lock. She turned as Ryan entered the apartment and shut the door behind him, his gaze searching for her and then smiling slightly as he found her, hovering near the fireplace.

She couldn't think of a thing to say to him. 'Got it taken care of?' she asked, and could have bitten out her tongue at the idiocy of it.

He looked amused. 'Yes, were you worried?' he said, gently teasing, as he came away from the door. She backed away and went to the window to look over the street. After a moment, he commented, very casually, 'I haven't a thing in my refrigerator. I suppose I should go and pick up some groceries. How about going out to eat tonight?'

'Sounds fine,' she said tonelessly, unable to look at him.

A pause. 'Good. Well, would you like to come shopping with me, or would you rather stare at the traffic?'

That question had been rather sharp to be exactly nice, and she spun around to stare at him with narrowed, assessing eyes. But his expression was bland enough, so she relaxed and replied, 'I'd rather come.'

The rest of the afternoon was spent shopping. They browsed through bookshops, a jewellery store, a novelty shop. Only towards the later part of the afternoon did they buy groceries, and when they finally let themselves back into his apartment and put away the food, it was time to think about changing for supper.

Devan quickly showered and then changed into a cream trouser suit while Ryan washed and also dressed. She applied blusher to her cheekbones and a dark blue shadow thinly over her lids while Ryan dried his wet hair and then came back to his bedroom. He regarded her for a long, disturbing moment before asking, 'All set?'

They ate at a local Italian restaurant, and, as they relaxed afterwards they chattered about light, inconsequential things while Devan felt more and more disorientated and miserable. Finally they headed back to his apartment once more, and Ryan let her precede him through the opened door.

Devan moved aimlessly through the living room, touching things lightly with her fingers, not stopping at any one place. She heard and felt him not far from her, breathing quietly, watching her wander. 'All right,' he said, and his tone was flat. It made her jump, visibly. 'What is it, Devan? You've been this way all day long.'

'What way?' she asked, turning to look at him, stalling.

He looked grim and tired as he leaned against the end of his couch and crossed his arms. He also looked immovable, as sturdy as a rock. 'Uncommunicative, moody, restless, uneasy, jumpy,' he said succinctly. 'Need I go on?'

She eyed him with a dull resentment. 'No, I think you've about covered it,' she replied drily. Her eyes filled, suddenly glazing bright in the light of the table lamp, and she whirled away so that he wouldn't see.

But he had, and he asked very quietly, 'What's wrong? Don't you know by now that you can talk to me?'

And suddenly she could, for he was the Ryan she had known in Maine after all, and not such a stranger. He was listening and patient and caring, and she turned back around to face him. 'I'm scared,' she said, and her voice caught on the words. 'I don't know what the hell I'm doing here. I don't like this, I feel confused, and I want to go back. This isn't going to work.'

'My God,' he said wearily, and his face showed a sudden, startling anger as he pushed off the couch and strode for her. He retorted, his light eyes flashing. 'Do you think you have a corner on the market of uncertainties here? Do you have any idea what it took me to invite you in the first place? I've never lived with a woman in my life! I waited two days for you to make up your mind, and now I've got to wait for you to be happy about it!' He made a visible effort to get back in control. 'What's wrong with this place? Tell me. Maybe I can change it.'

He was impatient with her, and she couldn't blame him. She looked around her as if seeing everything for the first time, but of course that couldn't be, for spilling wetness dashed down her cheeks, blindingly. But she offered, her voice quavering, 'It's a lovely apartment.'

He sighed heavily, and came slowly over to cup her face between his hands, his thumbs gently rubbing at her cheeks, streaking across the path of tears. 'It's me, isn't it?' he asked, still with that weary tone, now quite patient.

His touch had her grasping at his wrists in tight desperation, feeling the solidity of bone and muscles and tendon, holding on to him like a lifeline. 'No,' she whispered, and drew her next breath in on a sob. 'It's me. I'm not the same person I was four years ago. I—I need something I can hang on to. I need something to hold, to depend on. I'm afraid the rug's going to be pulled out from under my feet, and the world is going to shift again. I thought I could take your offer. I thought I could try to build something here, in the same way I had with Lee. But I don't want that. I can't.'

He pulled her forward and held her head against his chest. She felt his cheek laid against her hair, rubbing, while one hand left her own cheek to circle her waist. Then she was clinging to his shirt and hiding her face in him, feeling the rise and fall of his breathing. She didn't stop to marvel that the very person who could frighten her could also give so much support and comfort.

'What will it take for you to believe in me?' he asked, and she could hear the note of sadness in his voice. 'Time? We've got that, if you can push past your fears. A personal reference? I can get one that says I don't get drunk, or throw drug parties, and that I'm a steady, hard worker. Support? I've given you that in the last three years. I think you know by now how highly I respect you and admire your work.'

'I—need security,' she whispered, with great difficulty.

He went still, as though shocked. 'Marriage?' he asked, and the shock was in his voice. Then he drew back and stared down at her, his eyes huge and dark. 'It's so soon, I didn't dare think of asking—is that what you meant?'

She broke away from his hold and escaped to the other side of the room. 'No!' she cried, and then, 'I don't know! God, I don't know!' She dug the heels of her hands into her eyes.

He took a step after her, and then another. 'I'll marry you if that's what it takes to get you to trust me,' he said. His hand went out, strangely pleading. 'I'll marry you and be that something for you to hang on to. Hold on to me, Devan.'

Her back was to him, and she tilted back her head to stare at the ceiling. Her voice coming broken, she whispered, 'For ever and ever. You could make a decision like that after only a week? To me? Oh, Ryan, what are you doing to me? Why do you come out of nowhere and turn me around until I don't know if I'm coming or going? I'm starting to live again inside, and I don't know if I can take all this emotion you're pulling from me. I don't even know how you feel about me; all I know is what I feel and think, and that's what is scaring me half to death.'

'I love you,' he whispered starkly. 'I'm in love with you. I want you to feel secure, and safe and warm and dry. I want to marry you because I want to, selfishly, for no other reason. I don't know you very well, and I want to know you intimately.'

She turned to look at him, her lips parted as she listened, dazed, to what he was saying. When he stopped, looking quite pale, she said, quite distressed, 'I threw water on you.'

He answered as if she had made perfect sense, 'I dried, didn't I?'

'I'm afraid that I would be a failure,' she then said baldly, baring herself to the core without even caring, indeed, needing to. 'And I don't want to hurt you that way.'

'How could you fail?' he said tenderly, as he took in her widened, frightened eyes, and the fragile hope dawning. 'You haven't failed at anything in your life. You only thought you had.'

'I'm thirty years old.'

'And I'm going to be forty, the sun has set outside, and next month will be August. What does any of it have to do with what we're discussing?'

'What—if I never write again?' she whispered then.

He blinked a moment. 'I bring in a pretty hefty pay cheque,' he said in reply. 'We wouldn't starve.'

That brought a flashing image of her bank account and how he surely must know what a great deal she was worth already, and, in spite of herself, she threw back her head and laughed. He smiled slightly in response and moved over to stare out at the street below. The living room lamp was the only light on, and he was in shadow at the other end of the apartment, which strangely didn't seem at all frightening to her now. His face was lit from blue shadow to a white, moving light from the traffic below.

'Take your time deciding,' he said to her on a sigh. 'There's no pressure. God, if it's one thing we do have, it's plenty of time. Time to get to know each other better, time to back out if that's what you really want, nothing but time.'

Yes, she knew that. She had often felt the burden of time on her shoulders this last year, and the feeling of futility at how she wasted it. But suddenly the future began to glow ahead of her, full of promise, and light, and warmth. She walked over to him and sank into a chair that was pushed to the wall by the window. He still looked tired, but now he also looked peaceful, once again content to wait for her.

She reached out her hand and laid it flat against his thigh, feeling the hard muscle under silken cloth, and his body warmth. As she stroked him lightly, he looked at her, and she said with great tenderness, 'You. Your understanding, your concern. Your sympathy, your caring, your integrity. How could I not love you? You were a stranger, and yet you took the time and effort to yank me out of the rut I was in, whether I wanted it or not. Nobody asked you to do it. Don't you know that, if I could, I'd give you the world?'

He squatted close to her chair, and brought her hand to his lips. 'I don't need the world. I just want my corner of it, with you. And maybe a honeymoon in the Bahamas.'

Another burble of laughter coming from her, unexpected and rich. Her heart expanded to hold all the swelling joy and delight she felt, and she wondered fleetingly if her chest would burst. She reached with her free hand to touch the side of his face, watching it gentle incredibly at the feel of her fingers, cool and light. 'You are unfathomable,' she said quietly, and he looked rather puzzled at that.

'Because I want a honeymoon in the sun?'

'No, because you could look at me the way I was, and love me anyway. You actually want me.'

'It's not a great mystery,' he whispered. 'I'm astonished you haven't seen it already. Didn't Janie and Gary's reaction to your departure give you a clue? Didn't the deep and passionate joy in your writing give you a clue? Helen knows. She's a lovely lady, but she can't hold a candle to your warmth and intensity of feeling. I looked at you and saw through your misery at what you were able to feel for your sister, and the children, and I wanted you to learn to care for me, too. I knew that if you could radiate your pain so clearly, then you would radiate your love in just the same way, marvellously, magnificently.' She watched, rapt, as the silver white lights flickered across his shadowed face, bringing those mature features into sharp focus, bringing those light eyes to brilliance. And then he looked at her and smiled, a slow, sweet spreading of his lips, and she was not at all surprised to find it to be one of the most beautiful sights of her life. It etched itself with a delicate permanence into her mind. 'So you see,' he said. 'It is very simple. I hope to keep warm by your love for the rest of my life.'

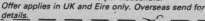

 **ROMANCE**

AND THEN HE KISSED HER...

This is the title of our new venture — an audio tape designed to help you become a successful Mills & Boon author!

In the past, those of you who asked us for advice on how to write for Mills & Boon have been supplied with brief printed guidelines. Our new tape expands on these and, by carefully chosen examples, shows you how to make your story come alive. And we think you'll enjoy listening to it.

You can still get the printed guidelines by writing to our Editorial Department. But, if you would like to have the tape, please send a cheque or postal order for £2.95 (which includes VAT and postage) to:

AND THEN HE KISSED HER...

To: Mills & Boon Reader Service, FREEPOST, P.O. Box 236, Croydon, Surrey CR9 9EL.

Please send me _____ copies of the audio tape. I enclose a cheque/postal order*, crossed and made payable to Mills & Boon Reader Service, for the sum of £_____.

*Please delete whichever is not applicable.

Signature _____

Name (BLOCK LETTERS) _____

Address _____

_____ Post Code _____